Liam at Large

Joseph McKeown

CORGI BOOKS

Dedicated to the memory of
My Father.

LIAM AT LARGE

A CORGI BOOK 0 552 12799 X

First publication in Great Britain

PRINTING HISTORY
Corgi edition published 1986

Copyright © Joseph McKeown 1986

This book is set in 10/11pt Paladium.

Corgi Books are published by Transworld Publishers Ltd.,
61-63 Uxbridge Road, Ealing, London W5 5SA,
in Australia by Transworld Publishers (Aust.) Pty. Ltd.,
15-23 Helles Avenue. Moorebank. NSW 2170, and in New
Zealand by Transworld Publishers (N.Z.) Ltd., Cnr. Moselle
and Waipareira Avenues, Henderson, Auckland.

Made and printed in Great Britain by
Hunt Barnard Printing Ltd., Aylesbury, Bucks.

Foreword

Merseyside 1934.

My name is Liam, I am fourteen. I come from the slums.
I have nothing, no skills, little learnin' and no prospects,
please mister can you give me a job, *any* job . . . Please, me
Mam needs the money.

"Yeh kiddin' son . . . bugger off."

1

Happy Release

"Well, what y' gonna do?"

Dad's question caught me completely unawares as I sat munching a piece of bread and dripping at the kitchen table. I looked uncertainly at Mam on my left, then shrugged helplessly. Less than an hour earlier I had walked through the school gates for the last time. Free at last — but was I? All my elation at leaving vanished with Dad's blunt question. With him still unemployed, the family living on a food ticket, and Con, my eldest brother, ostensibly living with Aunt Min but creeping in and out of the house like a fugitive to avoid the Means Test man, things were almost as bad as they had been eighteen months before during the unemployed riots. I looked at Mam's drawn face anxiously. The previous winter had been savage. With four adults and two children dead within the four streets that made up our district, we had all staggered into the spring sunshine by the skin of our teeth and, with every penny counting, the moment they had anxiously waited for had arrived, I was finally free to work full time.

I had of course, like all the other kids, worked part-time for pennies since I was about nine but this was for *real*. I had to get a job and *quick*, but where, doing what? With tradesmen like Dad and Con walking the streets what the hell chance did I have with no skills, the bare minimum of education and a couple of thousand like me ready to slit my throat to get in first? The last of my euphoria vanished as I looked into his worried eyes.

"I dunno," I said defensively.

"Well you'd better bloody find out 'adn't y'?" he snapped, "Y' can't just 'ang around can y'?"

"Ah give 'im a chance," broke in Mam. "He's only just left y'know." He ignored her.

"Ave y' looked?" he asked. I hesitated. With my part-time job at the butcher's I hadn't had much time, but I had tried one place on the off chance.

"Yeah, I asked at the timber yard."

"Which one?"

"The one up the dock road, y'know, at the North End."

Mam looked worried. It was a rough area.

"What d'y' wanna go there for?" he queried, "It's a long walk . . . anyroad" he added before I could speak, "What did they say?"

"Bugger off." Mam's eyes popped as I answered flatly.

"Y'what?" he snarled. I tensed. None of the children had ever been allowed to swear at home.

"That's what the fella said," I explained, "I asked 'im for a job an' 'e said 'bugger off', so I did."

"The cheeky sod," exclaimed Mam, "What a bloody way t' treat a kid askin' for a job."

"What d'y' expect," said Dad bitterly, "We're nuthin' but dirt nowadays. He'll 'ave t' get used t' that."

"D'y' think Harry'll take y' on full time?" she asked anxiously. Quietly I dropped another bombshell.

"I've already got the sack," I said diffidently, "I finished today."

She sat bolt upright. The one and sixpence I received from Harry had been a vital part of the family income for the past two years.

"Jesus," she exclaimed, "*why*?"

"Said 'e couldn't afford t' keep me now I'd left school."

"Why the 'ell didn't y' *tell* me?" she demanded. Butty still in my hand I gazed at her miserably and wished to God I hadn't left school.

"I didn't like to," I said quietly. Words seemed to fail her.

"Jesus," she repeated.

"Typical," cried Dad in sudden temper, "Bloody typical."

10

"Can't 'e keep y' on at the same wages 'til y' find somethin' else?" she asked agitatedly.

" 'enry's already got the job." I daren't tell her that I had tipped Henry, one of the gang and a year younger than me, that I was going to finish. Anyway I was so keen to get out of school I hadn't even thought about getting a job. I wish I had kept my mouth shut and hung on but it was too late.

"What're we gonna do?" she asked helplessly. Dad shrugged as he looked at me.

"You'll 'ave t' get somethin' Li, even if it's only a few coppers." Per'aps it'll be easier for you. They don't 'ave t' pay kids much even if they are full time." His eyes suddenly gleamed.

"Hey warrabout the bakers? Y' used t' like it there." Mam brightened immediately.

"Yeah," she said enthusiastically "Why don't y' try it? Y' never know, y' might touch."

I looked from one to the other uncertainly. The bakehouse had been alright when I worked as a tally lad during junior school, but who wanted to be a tally boy at *fourteen*. True it was dead easy, all one had to do was to wait at the top of the bakehouse steps until the women brought their rolls of dough in the tins provided by the baker; you gave them one metal tally with a number on, then stuck its twin into the dough and put the tin into the first or second baking line according to what the customer wanted. After the baking I just handed them the bread in exchange for the tally. Cushy as it was I didn't fancy it as my life's work.

"Well?" she queried impatiently.

"Aw . . . I dunno, I . . ."

"Get round there," snapped Dad.

"What *now*?"

"Yeah now. If there is anythin' goin' 'alf the kids in the street'll be round there before mornin'. Y' not the only one 'ose just left y'know."

"Can I . . ."

"Finish y' butty an' git," he snapped, "If there's a job, take it *warrever* 'e offers."

Five minutes later I was on my way. In fifteen I was back, triumphant.

"Just beat Fatty Boyle to it," I exclaimed gleefully as I came through the door to an expectant audience.

"There," exclaimed Dad, "What did I tell y'? Y' gorra be quick on y' feet these days lad, just remember that."

"Ow much?" asked Mam.

"Three and a tanner a week." I announced triumphantly, "An' Old Foggerty said I could 'ave a coupla balm cakes every day." Dad laughed.

"Well y' won't retire on it, but it's a start, and," he added bitterly, "you'll 'ave a job which is a damned sight more'n I 'ave."

"What time d'y start?" asked Mam.

"Seven o'clock tomorrer." She gasped.

"Seven o'clock! God almighty, that's early isn't it?"

"It's a bake'ouse," said Dad scornfully, "Of course it's early, 'e'll 'ave t' get used t' that. What time d'y' finish?" I looked at him dumbly.

"I didn't ask, I just wanted the job."

"Don't worry, you'll learn lad, and quick."

At five minutes to seven I was in the overpowering heat of the bakehouse, fully expecting to take up where I had left off four years before. I headed for the stairs leading to the street door where I used to sit with the tally box.

"Where y' goin'?" asked the boss.

"To open the door for the tallies," I replied, glancing at the shelf where the tally box used to be kept.

"No tallies now lad, all cash customers." I looked across at Fred the assistant, busily working two lumps of dough. He grinned.

"S'right Li. Only Christmas bunloaves on tallies nowadays."

Suddenly the boss got irritable.

"Come on lad, no time for gassing. Fetch that sack over to the mixer."

12

Seconds later, legs shaking with effort, I dragged the half-filled sack towards the new electric mixer and under Fred's instructions filled it. Before I knew it it was time for the first baking to come out of the oven. Twice I nearly got brained as they expertly whipped out the red-hot loaves on the long handled wooden spades and dumped them on the long table. Hands covered with sacking I tried desperately to keep up with them as I banged the tins to loosen the bread. I jumped a foot as Foggerty suddenly roared impatiently down my ear.

"Come on, for Christ's sake, move it lad. We 'aven't got all day . . . 'ere, come on, I'll tip, you stack."

I shook the sacking off and began to stack the steaming bread in neat rows ready for throwing through the trap-door overhead into the shop.

"Right," called Fred, "That's the lot," Foggerty jerked his thumb upwards.

"Up y' get lad an' catch." I looked at him dazedly. I felt shattered and uncertain, as tally lad I never did know what happened to the bread after it came out of the oven.

"Well," he snapped. "What are y' waitin' for? . . . 'urry up."

"Go on Li," said Fred gently. "Open the trap, the missus'll tell y' what t' do."

He winked sympathetically as I turned and shot up the stairs. Moments later, breathless and sticky with sweat I hurled myself into the shop and straight into the massive Mrs Foggerty. Instead of the cheerful grin I had known, her face wrinkled in a scowl as she hitched her ample bosom clear of the whalebone line and snapped my head off.

"Luk where y' flamin' well goin' will y'?, an' get that trap open, customers is waitin'."

I looked at the restless queue beginning to build up, dashed for the trap and nearly ruptured myself lifting the heavy door. A split second later two two-pound loaves hurtled through and hit me in the chest then dropped back. Foggerty's voice boomed from below.

"What the 'ell are y' doin' up there? . . . Y' supposed t' *catch* the bloody things not chuck 'em back." I heard

13

Fred's muffled laugh. Next moment Mrs Foggerty loomed over me and leaned over the trap.

"Cut the bloody swearin' Albert," she hissed, "There's customers in."

"What the 'ell d'y' want me t' do woman?" roared Foggerty, "*congratulate* 'im? . . . Stand by up there," he added menacingly. "An' this time *don't* miss."

I concentrated like mad as the Missus stood waiting to catch from me. Loaves came through the trap as though fired from a gun. Unfortunately the Missus tried to serve an impatient customer. It was fatal. She turned as I threw. The loaves bounced off her. Suddenly it was chaos, as loaves continued to come. I daren't hold them and didn't have the sense to stop him. As fast as they came I chucked them like a scrum half. Flushed and confused she tried to stack.

"Mr Foggerty . . . Mr Foggerty," I yelled desperately as the loaves mounted around her, " 'ang on a minute."

"Y' what?" he yelled, still throwing. I couldn't cope. As I staggered back exhausted, two crispy browns by the look of them, flashed past me and headed for the ceiling. It was too much. With the customers in fits, Mrs Foggerty finally lost her gentility.

"For Christ's sake Albert," she yelled, "Stop it will y'."

"Y'what?" came the shrill cry from below. It was the last straw. She jammed me hard against the shelf as she grabbed the door and slammed it shut.

Minutes later, sweat streaked, hair awry and covered in crumbs, the boss appeared at the door and gazed open mouthed at the heap of bread, on, under and round the counter.

"Christ almighty," he exclaimed. His homicidal look turned to me and he flicked his head towards the door.

"I wanna word with you," he said menacingly.

God how I wished I was back at school. It augered ill for my future career.

" 'ow did y' gerron?"

It was half past eight. Mam and I were enjoying the two balm cakes promised as part of my salary in the half-hour break I was given between first and second bakings. I felt shattered but excited at the prospect of going out on the rounds when I got back. She nearly choked on the balm cake when I explained what had happened.

"What did 'e say?"

"Cor, 'e wasn't 'alf wild." I replied, remembering the boss, crimson faced as he lectured me.

"Don't worry." advised Mam "You'll settle, they're not bad, the Foggertys."

"It's not 'alf different to when I was tally lad." She looked at me knowingly.

"Don't worry, you'll get nuthin' for nuthin', you'll work for y' wages, but just keep y' nose clean an' you'll be alright. What y' doin' next anyroad?"

"Deliverin'," I said proudly. She looked concerned. "With a basket?" I nodded.

" 'Ow many loaves at a time?"

"Twenny-four." She gasped.

"Y' can't carry that many, you'll kill y'self." I laughed light heartedly.

"They're on a bike," I explained.

"But you can't ride a bike."

"They don't know that . . . anyroad I can soon learn can't I?"

She put the remains of the balm cake on the table, deep concern on her face. "Suppose'n y' fall off?" I began to feel a little irate but daren't show it even though I was fourteen. I changed the subject and held up my foot admiringly.

"Boots are nice aren't they?" I stated, "Fit nice too."

She looked at the boots bought for a few coppers the previous night to avoid having to wear my Sunday ones for work.

"They're alright," she said despondently, "Keep y' feet warm anyroad."

I rose from the table to avoid further discussion on the bike.

"Now for God's sake be careful," she admonished as I turned to go, "If y' fall off then push it."

Without the slightest intention of being so easily defeated I promised I would. The bike, when I got back, looked monstrous with its fully-loaded basket weighing heavily on the tiny front wheel. The missus gave me a list of calls, then looked from me to the bike.

"Are y' sure y' can manage it?" she asked, doubt in her rheumy blue eyes.

"Yeah easy," I said, staggering under its weight as I moved it from the wall. "I'll walk it down the road a bit t' get outa the traffic."

She wasn't listening. Already on her way back into the shop, she stopped and turned. The bike leaned heavily against me as I listened.

"Remember," she warned, waving a podgy finger at me, "No *tick*, cash only. Y' should 'ave four bob when y' get back . . . lose any an' I'll stop it outa y' wages."

I nodded. "Miserable sod," I thought.

I cleared the main road then tried my luck down the first quiet street I came to. It was disaster. With one foot on the pedal I hopped along desperately, then tried to mount. The small wheel in the front hit a brick and, top heavy, the whole caboodle turned turtle. There were loaves everywhere and less than fifty yards away a railway horse lumbered towards me with its heavy load.

Frantically I jammed the bike against the nearest wall and raced against time to clear the road before the wagon came. I made it with seconds to spare, then bruised and shaken, stood open mouthed as the wagon stopped. There was a tinkle of water as the horse relieved itself. The driver grinned.

"That shook y'," he said amiably.

One by one, with fear clutching at my heart I examined the loaves. Three hours into my professional career and already I was sick of the sight of bread. I was lucky, except for one or two with a cockeyed look they weren't too bad. Thank God the road was dry. I sighed with relief then immediately got another shock, the chain was off. I looked at it desperately. I couldn't touch it. Even I knew that oily bread wasn't good for trade. I had to push.

Two hours later, arms aching from steadying the bike and with four loaves left where customers hadn't had the tuppence to pay for them, I staggered back into the shop for the next round, but fate hadn't finished with me. I was a penny short in my money.

Mrs Foggerty looked at me suspiciously.

"Y' short." she snapped. I gazed at her horrified. I had been as careful as I could, and had even ticked the list as they paid.

"That's all I've got . . . *honest*," I replied pleadingly.

"You'll 'ave t' make it up at the end of the week, I'll mark it down," she said, suiting the action to the words. My heart dropped. All the joys of full-time work vanished. If I kept this up I'd be paying *her* at the end of the week.

The second and third rounds I didn't even try to ride until all the loaves had gone, but I *did* learn to ride. At five o'clock, battered, exhausted but triumphant, I arrived home. I couldn't wait to tell the gang about the bike. They were all there when I arrived at our old winter headquarters near the undertaker's yard.

"What y' done t' y' legs?" asked Sniffer Johnson, madder than ever now that he had left school and landed a job in a greengrocer's.

"Nuthin'," I said as the remainder, all newly out of school except Henry Fielding who had taken my job at the butchers, eyed my lacerated legs.

"What d'y' mean?" demanded Sniffer picking his nose contemplatively, "Y' didn't do that scratchin' y'self did y'? Come on, what 'appened?"

"Fell off me bike that's what," I snapped. Sniffer screeched with laughter.

"Aw shurrup Sniffer will y'. Y' like a bloody banshee." Every eye turned to Dinny as the scraggy tousled-headed figure slumped disconsolately on one of the half dozen crates that served as furniture.

"What's up with you?" I asked.

"What's up," he repeated disgustedly, "I'll tell y' what's up mate, I'll do that old sod before I've finished, that's what."

We looked at him sympathetically. His boss at the market stall for the past year was a noted slave driver with a temper as short as the money in my Mam's purse and Dinny, a year older than me, was forever in trouble with him.

"What 'appened this time?" I asked, refusing the battered dog end he offered me.

"Nuthin'," he said irately, "There I was skinnin' sheeps 'eads as fast as I could go when 'e clips me over the flamin' ear. " 'Urry up he says. What d'y' think y' are, a bloody surgeon or sommat? Get them flamin' 'eads done quicker or y' cin 'ave y' cards.''

"I thought, 'Right mate, I'll 'ave you,' so I stuck a coupla sheep's eyes down Lizzie's dress."

The shed rocked with laughter, I could imagine the effect on Mr Wilson's podgy fifteen-year-old daughter.

"I'll bet that made 'er 'op a bit," I said, forgetting my own aches and pains in the merriment.

"Y' kiddin'," said Dinny with relish. "She screamed blue bloody murder. She 'ad 'alf the market up rushin' up an' down the aisles screamin', 'They're in me draws, they're in me draws.' "

"They wouldn't see nuthin' down there," opined Sniffer, screeching at his own joke.

"What 'appened then?" broke in Henry's quiet voice from the corner.

"Got the flamin' sack didn't I?"

"What'll y' Mam say?" I asked, knowing how vital the money, and especially the bits of meat were to their large family. He grinned.

"Aw don't worry," he said winking and tapping the side of his nose, "I gorrit back alright, I don't keep me eyes open for nuthin' y'know!"

"What d'y' mean?" asked Bonko Armfield. Dinny winked.

18

"Diddlin' the customers . . . Oh we all know y'know, we've watched 'im stickin' weights under the meat durin' the rush on Saturdays when 'es weighin' out. Anyroad I gorrit back. What's your job like? Still on the tallies?"

"Y' kiddin', they don't do tallies no more, I've gorra do *everythin'*."

"What do y' mean?" asked Henry softly. Henry always spoke softly. Actually he was far too gentle to be in the gang but he had always been with us and he made an ideal *front* man, especially for getting free rides on the ferries. He was so gentle, so innocent you would think butter wouldn't melt in his mouth. With just one penny between us all, he would put on his fainting act near the ferry ticket office. It never failed. The collector would shoot out to see to him and the rest of us would whip under the barrier, down the floating bridge like the clappers and, since tickets were only paid for on the Birkenhead side we could get free rides for hours just by hiding when the boat tied up on either side of the river. Like myself, a Catholic, his greatest ambition was to be a priest, but with his family as poor as Lazarus I didn't fancy his chances.

"Well," I continued to the interested audience, "I've gorra carry sacks, stack the bread, deliver it . . . y'know *everythin'*."

"What d'y' mean, stack the bread?" asked Bonko. I told them. The shed rocked anew with laughter as I explained about the bread coming through the trap.

"You'd berra learn quick," suggested Bonko, "Or you'll be out on y' ear like me."

We looked at him puzzled. Like me he had only started that morning.

"What d'y' mean *like me*?" asked Dinny.

"I got the sack too."

"What for?" As leader of the gang I was concerned for him.

"I ate some biscuits, y'know, broken ones."

"Aye," said Dinny sarcastically, "But 'oo broke 'em?" Bonko grinned.

"Ave y' told y' Mam yet?" I asked. He shook his head.

"She'll 'ave me liver." I could imagine it. She was a big woman with eight kids to feed and, like my own Mam, had looked forward to Bonko earning a few bob. We had to do something to make the money up to him until he got another job, but *what*?

" 'ave y' been 'ome yet?" I asked.

"Y' kiddin. Warram I gonna tell 'er? Anyroad y'know what me Dad's like, 'e'll batter me." Yes we knew alright, Mr Armfield was a strict disciplinarian and Bonko had had the weals on his back many a time to prove it.

"Why tell 'em?" asked Dinny. I looked at him puzzled. He was usually a rock of sense.

" 'es gorra tell 'em 'asn't 'e?" I said irately. "What'll 'is Mam say if 'e doesn't bring 'is wages 'ome Friday? She'll know then won't she?"

"Not if we make it up for 'im she won't. Then 'ell 'ave time t' look for sommat else won't 'e? If 'e touches they'll never know, will they?"

It was a great idea with just one snag. Where the hell would *we* get the money?

"How much are y' gerrin'?" I asked.

"Two and a tanner an' a couple of cabbages if I want 'em."

Two and sixpence, hell's bells, we wouldn't have that much between the lot of us at the weekend. I said so.

"Warrabout workin' the bottles again?" asked Dinny, "Its only Monday, we've got till Friday an' there's plenty'a shops arn't there?"

"Warrabout 'orsemuck," asked Sniffer, serious for once. I shook my head.

"Too slow. You've gotta 'ave buyers for that. Anyroad, me barrer's broke."

Collecting horsemuck and selling it to gardeners just on the edge of town was definitely out. The horses couldn't be relied on to perform regularly and with no barrow for transport we were up the creek.

"No, bottles is the quickest." stated Dinny with all the wisdom of his fifteen years. "If we work it right we should make at least a tanner t'night then we'll 'ave plenty of time, 'e might gerra job termorrer anyroad."

"Yeah, pigs might fly," broke in Sniffer cheerfully.

"Right," I said. "That's settled then, but no shares this time OK?, everythin' in is for Bonk, fair enough?"

Everyone agreed to drop the normal practice of equal shares with a penny extra for the front man, which was usually Henry who handed the bottles in at the shop counter whilst we pinched them out of the yard at the back if we could. With most shops giving a penny on all returned bottles it was a handy trade in emergencies like this.

"OK with you Hen?" He nodded agreement, and I split the gang into two squads.

"Watch out for the scuffers," I warned. "We're not at school now y'know so if we're caught we'll be for the 'igh jump." They nodded silently. Gone were the days when a policeman would march us home to our parents for punishment if we were caught nicking bottles or free riding on the back of tramcars. If we were caught now it would be court, even the birch. I shuddered to think what would happen to me at home if I was caught and taken up. It was a toss up whom I feared most, Dad or the Judge.

"We'll be alright," said Dinny authoritatively, "Anyway," he added with a nod at Bonko, "If we don't 'e'll be for it off 'is ole man and no mistake."

By seven o'clock we were back in the shed. Things had gone as smooth as a nut and the kitty enlarged by nine-pence. A couple of more nights like that and Bonko was safe. All he had to do was to spin them a good yarn at home about his new job when he handed it in on Friday, the trick was to get another before the following Monday. It was a hectic week and I was glad when Saturday arrived. Bonko landed a job on the Thursday and I got my three and sixpence, less fourpence stoppages for one loaf ruined and two pennies lost on the round. Still, it wasn't a dead loss, Mam got the ruined loaf with my pay.

I can still see her watching me come up the yard with

the small bag of coppers I had earned. I held the bag out to her as I approached but she turned and walked into the house and waited for me to come in.

"Are y' alright?" she asked, as I sat down wearily. There was a strange awkwardness between us as I laid the coins on the table.

"There y'are," I said triumphantly. "Three an' tuppence. . . . Mr Foggerty stopped fourpence cause I lost tuppence and busted that loaf there," I nodded at the battered loaf. She sat down opposite to me.

"What are y' gonna do with it?"

"What d'y' mean?, the *loaf*?" She laughed.

"No y' fool, the money." She nodded towards the coppers.

"It's for you," I said, surprise in my voice. She shook her head.

"You earned it Li, its up t' you." I was nonplussed. With not a penny in the house she hesitated to take it, *why*?

"But I got it for you," I said, feeling strangely tense.

"I know *that*," she said. "But you earned it so tell me what y' want out of it, that's fair isn't it?"

"No," I protested, "I don't need any." That was a black lie and she knew it. A smile crossed her face.

"Will y' take a shillin' then?" I gasped, a *shilling*, God almighty I would hardly know what to do with it. I shook my head.

"Would sixpence be too much?" I ventured. She laughed and pushed six pennies towards me.

"Alright then, sixpence it is. Is that fair?" I nodded. She gave me one of her rare hugs. I felt embarrassed. The deal was done and for the *second* time in my life I actually had sixpence I could call my own.

2

Rabbit 'oles

"Hey Li. What're we gonna do this afternoon?" asked Fatty Boyle half heartedly. I looked around the miserable faces in the shed. Overhead the rain battered down on the corrugated iron roof to emphasise the misery within.

It was more than four months since we had hurled ourselves gleefully through the school gates for the last time. Our impact on the world since that glorious day had been *nil* and with an errand boy's job as our highest attainable objective it looked like staying that way. Still, we had learned a lot, the main thing was that full-time work was not all that it was cracked up to be, even though three quarters of the adult population had spent years searching for it in vain. I had heard several times at school that slavery had been abolished, but they were kidding. If William Wilberforce had tried his hand at errand boy in the thirties he would have had to start his campaign all over again.

On the go from morning until night on a thousand different jobs. Treated like dirt and worked to a standstill for a maximum of between three and sixpence and five bob a week, all we needed was to paint our faces black, take a penny boat ride across the Mersey and stand in the old slave colonades at the Pier Head and we would have fitted the part to a tee.

True, all the gang, with the exception of Henry, had full time jobs, but with the wages of all five combined coming to a total of nineteen shillings and sixpence, (less stoppages) we were not exactly ecstatic. Tommy Rolf especially, who wanted to be a soldier, was restless and had changed jobs four times in as many months, against ruthless competition, to increase his pay to its present level of four bob. We weren't kids really, just crafty old men in short trousers. Anyway it was no good having ambitions, one look at us in our patched-up clothes, one sentence from our limited vocabulary and any employer, apart from giving us the most menial tasks, would split his sides laughing. I *know*, I tried it. *Why* I'll never know except that I heard Aunt Min say to Mam one night, "It's a pity Li couldn't 'ave gorran office job to improve himself."

She must have been kidding of course, but I fancied the idea. I had seen fellows strutting along in their natty suits, polished shoes and with *clean* hands and thought, "That's for me." So with all the innocence of the absolute ignorant, and without consulting anyone I tried my hand and waltzed confidently into the local office of the Co-op. Even as I record it I blush at the consequences. With hair still wet from the water I had used to slick it back for the great moment I stood quite unabashed before the counter. A girl of about seventeen asked me politely what I wanted.

"I wanna clerk," I said confidently. She looked puzzled.

"Which one?" It was my turn to look puzzled.

"Whaddy y' mean?" I asked. She flushed slightly.

"Which clerk do you want?" she repeated, indicating the bowed heads behind her. I shook my head vehemently. God she was thick, I thought.

"I don't want wanna *them*, I wanna *be* wanna them!" She gave up.

"One moment please." Rubbing her head gently she left the counter. Minutes later she was back with a tall, serious looking man of about forty. He eyed me up and down silently. Suddenly I felt uncomfortable. I was out of my depth. One or two heads raised and amused glances came my way. I began to wish I had never come.

"Yes?" he said quietly, "What can I do for you?" I repeated my request. A smile flickered across his pale face.

"Ah" he said, "I think I understand, "You want a

24

position as a clerk?"

I got his drift and nodded eagerly. He quietened a growing snigger behind him with a quick turn of the head.

"That's alright Miss Williams," he said quietly to the
girl, "I'll deal with this." He leaned confidentially over
the counter as she left. Quietly but gently he filled me in
on the facts of life. The message I got, though he never
said one word to embarrass me, was that I was ill dressed,
educationally as thick as a brick, with an address that
was equivalent to the zoo.

He was a real gent but, despite the fact that he actually
came round the counter, put his arm gently across my
shoulders and showed me out with the utmost politeness,
I felt so small I thought I would never reach the pedals of
my delivery bike parked outside. Even now I cringe at the
memory. Mam and Dad *never* knew of my attempt at
gentility, even as a man I could never bring myself to
mention it because by doing so I would have humiliated
them, but I had *learned* a lot. Until such times as I could
haul myself up by my bootlaces I would be dirt. I daren't
even tell the lads, they would have laughed and *that*
would have been fatal. I had been in a filthy mood ever
since and the rain battering on the roof didn't help.

"Hey Li, what's up with y'?. Wharra we gonna do?" the
piping voice said again.

I flung Fatty a filthy look. "Why don't you shut it?" I
snapped, "What *can* we do in this flamin' weather?"

"There's no need t' talk t' 'im like that', 'e only asked,"
snapped Dinny.

I glowered at him sullenly but remained silent. At fifteen
he looked what he was, rough, tough and resourceful,
and although we had had several fights over the years I
didn't want to fall out with him over nothing. Besides he
had gained a new respect in the gang since his announce-
ment an hour earlier that in a week's time he would start
work in the shipyard, the nearest thing to heaven we
could think of. How he had managed to get in God alone
knew, but that was Dinny all over.

"Aw," I replied, a note of apology in my voice, "It's bin wanna them weeks, y'know?"

"Can't we go down t' the docks or summat? There might be somethin' movin' there."

"Do us a favour Tom," piped up Bonko Armfield, "Whaddy y' think we are, flippin' ducks?"

For the first time a ripple of laughter swept the shed. We all felt nervy and irritable. Run off our feet all week, Sunday was the only day when the gang could meet and enjoy themselves together and now it was bucketing down.

"Hey Bonko," Jimmy Armfield looked across at the sound of Dinny's voice. His Mam went mad when we called him this but with his enormous nose it was a natural. Anyway he seemed very fond of his deformity, he certainly spent enough time picking it.

"Wharrabout the tunnel?" asked Dinny.

"Wharrabout it?"

"Biggest rabbit 'ole in England is that," opined Sniffer with a high pitched giggle. "Me Dad says they're trying t' find ferrets big enough t' catch 'em."

"Go on like that Sniff an' you'll finish up on the stage," said Bonko.

"Yeah," broke in Tommy sarcastically, "The *landin'* stage down at the ferry."

Dinny became irritable at the diversion.

"Luk, knock it off will yer, I ask a simple bloody question an' what do I get? A load of flamin' comedians. . . . Y' uncle's a cocky watchman down there isn't 'e?"

"So what?" asked Bonko.

"Is 'e on t'day?"

"Yeah why?"

"Just askin'."

"What d' y' wanna know for Din?" I asked.

"Jus' thought we'd 'ave a decko at it, y'know, close like."

I looked around the ragged band. With their best clothes, worn only for mass, now put safely away for the week, we looked what we were, slum kids. However innocent we were we always got chased on principle and Dinny knew it.

"Y' kiddin'," I said scornfully, "They wouldn't lerrus inside the gate, never mind down the tunnel and you know it."

"Bonko's uncle'd be there wouldn't 'e? We only wanna look at it, we're not gonna *pinch* the bloody thing are we?"

Sniffer screeched with delight at the thought. I vetoed the idea vehemently. Much as I would like to see it, it smelt of trouble and I had enough of that in the bake-house. The old sod had docked me a full sixpence on my last pay packet and twice in the week I had missed out on the balm cakes.

"Stuff the tunnel," I said. Much as I would like to have seen it I didn't want any trouble.

"There won't be any scuffers," persisted Dinny. "Besides we'll be with Bonko's uncle."

"What time is it?" asked Bonko suddenly.

"Round about twelve I reckon," said Henry. "Why?"

"Great," cried Bonko. "Uncle Joe'll be on 'is dinner time, an' I'll lay ten t' one 'es in the rub-a-dub."

"Which one?" asked Dinny.

"The Eagle, up by the tunnel."

I popped my head outside to see if it was still raining.

"Well?" asked Dinny, " 'as it stopped?"

"Near as makes no difference."

"Right," continued Dinny. "Warrabout it then, are we on?"

"OK," I replied, "Might as well, there's nuthin' else to do."

"Twenty minutes later, slightly damp, we stood outside the Eagle waiting for Bonko. Within minutes he was out.

"Jus' missed 'im, 'es gone back t' work."

" 'ow long ago?" asked Dinny.

"Feller said it was a wonder we didn't bump inter 'im. Come on let's catch 'im up."

We caught him within a few minutes, down a side street.

"Uncle Joe," yelled Bonko. The short middle-aged man turned.

27

'Hi ya Jim, whatcher doin'?''

"We wanna see the tunnel," announced Bonko flatly, "But every time we go near it they flippin' well chase us."

Uncle Joe rubbed his stubbly chin and shook his head uncertainly.

"I dunno Jim, they're a bit funny over kids on the site."

"Ah go on," pleaded Bonko, "Me mates 'aven't seen inside it."

He was wrong there, I had, but it was a long time ago.

"Go on Uncle Joe, honest we won't do nuthin'." Still he hesitated.

"Aw I dunno, anyroad what's the rush?, They're openin' the flamin' thing next month, y' cin see it then can't y'?"

"Well, it's not the same is it?" persisted Bonko. "There'll be crowds then."

I winked at Henry, our front man for any delicate negotiations. He winked back and turned his innocent blue eyes on Uncle Joe.

"Ah please Mr Armfield, go on, we won't do nuthin' t' get y' inter trouble. We'd love t' see it, wouldn't we lads, and it *is* Sunday. We wouldn't be in nobody's way would we?" Uncle Joe wavered. Go on *please*, you're the Cocky Watchman an' if *you* say we can then we can because you're really the sorta boss on Sundays aren't y'?"

We watched in silent admiration. In all the years I could remember I had never known him fail. I couldn't count the numbers of buttys he had cadged from workmen at the dock gates in the rough period before the riots. If ever he achieved his ambition of becoming a priest the devil wouldn't have a cat in hell's chance with him. I saw Dinny grin as Mr Armfield visibly wilted.

"Well I dunno," he said, resisting to the last. "Jobs is 'ard t' get an' I don't wanna lose this one."

"But you'll lose it anyway when it opens won't y'?" opined Dinny.

"We'll do *exactly* as you tell us," broke in Henry. "That's fair isn't it?"

For a further minute he wavered then capitulated with a threat.

"Alright then," he said resignedly. "But I warn y', the first sign of any bloody nonsense an' y' out, gorrit?"

Tingling with sudden excitement we nodded agreement, then I added my warning to his.

"Stick close," I ordered. "An' don't touch nuthin' otherwise Mr Armfield will be in dead trouble."

Minutes later we approached the palisade just at the back of the market, then passed through into another world. First we went to his tiny open fronted hut just inside the gates, and helped him stoke his coke fire, then our conducted tour began. It was a far cry from the huge circular hole I dimly remembered being clawed out of the ground on my first visit with Dad in 1926, just a year after it had started. Although still littered with tools and machinery, the chaos of that last visit had vanished. In its place was a clinical half circle of concrete and leading to it a wide concourse upon which, like green sentinels, stood four toll booths. The tunnel itself curved gently to the right down a gradual slope like some surrealistic pathway to the underworld. I gazed in awe as I took in every detail of this fantastic arrival in our midst. It was a long, long way from the charter received from King John by the local monks to ply the river, and whose ferry still stood less than a hoop and a holler from this new wonder, but I was puzzled. As a six year old I had seen a *full* circle as the hole was bored, now there was only a *half* circle. It seemed daft to me to dig a hole then only use half of it. I asked Uncle Joe what they had done with the other half.

" 'Ow the 'ell do *I* know?" he ejaculated. "These fellers isn't daft y'know. If they dug a hole they must've 'ad a bloody good reason, anyroad," he added, as though absolving himself from the disappearance of the vanished half, "It's nuthin' t' do with me."

By now we were actually inside the tunnel itself and I felt distinctly nervous. Bonko put my fears into words.

"Suppose'n the roof leaks?" he said, looking at the lines

of sunken roof lights vanishing into the distance.

"It won't," said Uncle Joe confidently, "It's reinforced. Anyroad, where it goes under the river it's *real* deep. I tell y' they're not daft."

"But won't the weight of the water break it?" asked Henry.

"I bloody 'ope not," said Uncle Joe emphatically, "If it does, it'll come out either end like the clappers an' no mistake."

"Yeah," pressed Bonko. "But suppose'n it did." Uncle Joe couldn't cope.

"Look Jim," he said exasperatedly, "I told y', that's not my job. All I gotta do is see no one nicks anythin'. I leave all that t' them that knows."

Still Bonko wasn't satisfied.

"But suppose'n a boat sank on top of it, *that* might bust it might'n it?"

"I keep tellin' y' y' silly bugger, they're not daft are they?"

"That's another thing," broke in Tom thoughtfully, "'ow did they get the 'ole from Liverpool t' meet the one from 'ere? Me Dad said they dug it from *both* ends at the *same* time. They couldn't *see* could they? Suppose they missed each other, what would 'ave 'appened then?"

Uncle Joe flicked his thumb at Tom.

"Cheerful sod isn't 'e?" he said to me. I grinned.

"Yeah," I replied. "But suppose'n they 'ad what would've 'appened?"

"Questions, questions," he exploded. " 'Ow the 'ell should I know what would 'ave 'appened? I'm a cocky watchman not a bloody engineer, they 'ad t' meet in the middle an' they *did* didn't they, so what the 'ell."

That was that. We couldn't get any more out of him.

"Come on." he said, an edge of nervousness in his voice, "I've taken a chance already. If any of the blockermen come sneakin' around I'll be in dead trouble, so come on, shift it. It'll be opened next month so then y' cin see it anytime y' like. Y' cin even see the King an' Queen when they open it."

"The *real* King an' Queen?", asked Henry.

"What the 'ell did y' think they were? . . . fairies? Course its the real King an' Queen. Luk, they're gonna sit up there."

He pointed to where the scaffolding was already being assembled on the far side of the market square for the Royal stand.

We never saw them of course. When the great day arrived the place was jammed with school children and the hoy polloi. The scruff were still working. It was to be nearly seven years before I eventually went through it, but what a sight when I did. It was well worth waiting for. Even now I get a thrill driving through it, but I still wonder what is underneath in the *other* half. You never know, it could be as Sniffer said — the biggest rabbit hole in England!

3

Fair Exchange

" 'ello Li, what're y' doin'?"

I looked up miserably at the sound of Aunt Min's familiar voice.

"Y' look as if you've lost a quid an' found a tanner," she added as I stopped under the shop awning and faced her.

"I've got the sack."

"Oh God, *no!*," she gasped. " 'Ave y' told y' Mam yet?" I shook my head, then gazed at the water cascading from the awning. If only it had stayed dry, I would have still been in a job. Sudden alarm ran through me.

"Don't tell 'er will y'?" I pleaded.

"She'll 'ave t' know Li," she said sympathetically. "There won't be no money on Friday will there?"

I nodded miserably as this cogent fact ran through my mind for the hundredth time since I returned to the shop, front wheel buckled, and the basket full of soggy bread, to face instant dismissal. I felt terrible. After nearly a year there old Foggerty wouldn't even listen, he just took one look at the bread and I got the bullet. I just couldn't face Mam at the moment, the three and sixpence a week was too important to her.

"Y' won't tell 'er Aunt Min will y'? . . . *please*, it's only Monday. Y' never know I might get somethin' and still get wages for the end of the week."

She pursed her lips. She knew even better than I did how vital the money was at home.

"Don't worry Li, I won't, that's your job, but don't leave it too late mind. Y' know y' Mam?"

Oh yes, I knew my Mam. I knew how she had to struggle

week in and week out to make ends meet. We didn't live, we existed and without my money it would be curtains for a week or two until she adjusted. Aunt Min flicked her shawl back over her shoulders and put her arm around me.

"Cheer up, it's not the end of the world y'know, . . . but," she warned, "If y' don't get somethin' by termorrer, tell 'er. She's not daft y'know. She'll know y' didn't do it on purpose . . . 'ere, go an' get y'self some sweets."

I took the proffered halfpenny thankfully.

"Don't forget," she warned as she drew her shawl around her ample shoulders, "Tell 'er the truth, she'll think more of y'. Where y' goin' anyway?"

"Well it's dinner time, I thought I'd see if Dinny was 'ome."

"Talk of the devil," she said with a laugh, "There 'e is over there, look."

I looked across the road in amazement. Sure enough, he was standing outside the barber's shop, left arm swathed in bandages. I was too shocked even to say cheerio to her.

"Hi ya Din," I yelled, skidding wildly towards him. He turned.

"What's the marrer?" I asked. He grinned.

"You'll never believe it."

"Try me."

"I fell over."

"Aw, come of it Din," I said disbelievingly. We bounced around so much as kids, on the walls, round the docks, and racing round the streets, we were more like rubber balls. I couldn't believe a simple fall could do that to him.

"Come on, what 'appened?"

"I tell y', I fell." He laughed, "Oh alright then, I fell over Maggie's feet at the hop last night. Y'know 'ow bloody awkward she is?"

It was my turn to laugh. Maggie Simpson, his latest conquest in his sudden passion for girls, was no nymph. All my troubles were temporarily forgotten as he described the tuppeny hop they had in the church hall after

Benediction the previous night. Apparently he was going great until Maggie stuck her foot out in a wild jig. He fell over it, stuck his hand out to save himself and broke a bone in his wrist. Still it could have been worse, she could have fallen on top of him.

"What're y' doin' 'ere?" I asked.

"Jus' bin t' the Panel t' sign on the sick, so I thought I'd 'ave a tuppenny all off," he jerked his thumb towards the barber's. "What're you doin' 'ere anyroad?"

"I got the poke."

" 'ell," he said feelingly, " 'ave y' told y' Mam yet?"

"Y' kiddin'. She'll 'ave a fit, I was just on me way round t' try an' see you. You've got y' ear t' the ground."

With the shop door half opened he looked at me and blew through his lips. "You'll be lucky," he said brutally.

Suddenly Mr Fenshaw, short on temper ever since we knew him, yelled at us.

"Hey you two," he roared, "If y' want y' flamin' 'air cut, come in, if y' don't, get t' 'ell outa there."

Meekly we went in and quickly closed the door as he glowered at us. He muttered something about kids to the customer in the chair as we sat down.

Ever since I could remember we had been to him for haircuts, well, not exactly haircuts, more a ritual scalping. They weren't known as tuppenny all offs for nothing. I think he must have served his apprenticeship in a prison or something. With his long curling moustache and fierce blue eyes he was a right martinet. As kids we hardly dared breathe during the operation. A sudden roar down our ear, and the regulation threat that he would have our ear off if we moved, was more than enough to keep the most restless kid still. Looking back I don't think it was such an idle threat either, he certainly nipped mine a time or two.

"What did y' get the sack for?" asked Dinny when we were comfortably seated.

"Smashed the order bike up."

" 'ell bells, 'ow?"

"Over the bridges, y'know what they're like when its wet?" He nodded. The bridges over the various docks were notorious amongst cyclists during wet weather, especially the railway lines that ran over them.

"Wha 'appened?"

"I skidded, the front wheel got stuck in the line, an' that was it, I went arse over 'ead." He burst out laughing, and drew a scowl from Mr Fenshaw.

"It's nuthin' t' laugh at, I 'ad two dozen flamin' loaves aboard. Blimey, y' shoulda seen it, bread all over the place, 'Orses stepping on them, lorries goin' over them, warra bloody mess."

"What did y' do?"

"What *could* I do?" I demanded. "The flippin' bell 'ad gone for a boat t' go through, I just 'ad t' grab what I could an' get t' 'ell outa it. A coupla dockers 'elped but it was no good, I finished up with a basket of soggy bread an' 'ad t' go back with it otherwise she've wanted the money for them."

"What did old Foggerty say?"

"Not a dicky bird. Poor old sod couldn't gerra word in edgeways. It was the missus that did all the talkin'."

"Did she sack y'?"

"No 'e did, she told 'im to."

"What did you do?"

"Neither of 'em would listen so I lost me rag an' told them t' stick their loaves where Paddy stuck 'is ninepence." Dinny laughed and again drew a scowl from Mr Fenshaw.

"What did she say t' that?"

"Nuthin'. I thought she was gonna choke when I left."

"What're y' gonna tell y' Mam?"

"You tell me, I reckon she'll 'ave me flamin' liver. Three an' a tanner's a lot t' lose ain't it?"

The conversation was cut short as Mr Fenshaw jerked his thumb at Dinny.

"Whadda y' want?" he asked as Dinny sat down in the chair. "A shave?"

"Trim," said Dinny hopefully. Mr Fenshaw grinned,

then, with expert snips of the scissors, waded in. Minutes later Dinny rose, his personality completely changed. In place of the unruly mat there was a uniform quarter inch bristle all over, except for a four inch regulation fringe in front.

"There y' are lad," said Mr Fenshaw, standing back to admire his work. "Y' won't get no nits in that."

"It'll save combin' too," added Dinny sarcastically.

Together we stepped outside. Dinny immediately clapped his hand to his bald head, but I beat him to it as I spat on my fingers and slapped them to his head.

"First wet," I said in the time honoured custom after a haircut.

"No need for first wettin'," he hissed as the rain lashed down, "Come on, let's go to the shed, I've got some apples stashed there."

We belted through the downpour to our headquarters, burst through the door and nearly fell over Bonko's outstretched legs as he sat morosely in the shadows.

"What the 'ell" yelled Dinny fighting to keep his damaged hand out of danger. "What y' doin' 'ere?"

Bonko, soaked to the skin, gazed miserably first at us then at the two battered wreaths lying on the floor.

"What're y' doin' with these?" I asked, picking one up and examining it.

"Deliverin' them," he replied miserably. "They're for a funeral this afternoon."

"Y' can't deliver *these*," I said, dropping the tangled mess to the floor. It suddenly dawned on him that I should have been at work.

"What's the marrer with you?" he asked, "sick?"

"Do I look flippin' sick?" I replied scornfully.

" 'e got the poke," explained Dinny.

"What for?"

"Never mind that," I snapped. "Warrabout the wreaths? Deliver them mate an' you'll get the poke too. What y' gonna do about 'em?"

"I dunno," he replied miserably, "I've bin tryin' t' fix

36

'em but they just seem t' get bloody worse."

"You can't fix them," broke in Dinny scornfully, "Them's done by experts mate. 'Ow the 'ell did y' gerrem in that state anyroad?"

"I was runnin' outa the rain an' fell on 'em, then every time I tried t' pick 'em up some silly bugger trod on 'em."

"Look Din," I snapped. "Never mind all that, warra we gonna do about 'em?"

My own troubles were momentarily forgotten in this new crisis. As we sat down in depressed silence it looked as though two of the gang would be unemployed if we didn't come up with something — and quick. One thing was certain, there was just no way we could fix the wreaths.

Suddenly Dinny slapped his knee with his good hand.

"Hey Li, whaddy y' think of this for an idea?"

"Go on."

"Well I know where there's a stack of wreaths, good un's too."

"Where?" asked Bonko eagerly.

"Where else?" cried Dinny triumphantly, "The cemetery!" I gasped.

"Aw come off it Din, y' take wreaths *to* the cemetery not *from* it. They'll think we're crackers."

"We're not gonna tell 'em are we?", he demanded in exasperation. "Look Li, Bonko's got t' deliver, right?" I nodded. "What time y' gorra gerrem there Bonk?"

" 'alf two. The funeral's at three."

"What the 'ell did y' start out so early for?" I demanded. "It's only 'alf ten now."

"Well I 'ad some other jobs t' do an' the boss said I could deliver 'em on me way."

"Right," said Dinny. "That's it. You go an' get y' other jobs done an' meet us back 'ere at two o'clock. Gorrit?"

"Warrabout the wreaths?"

"Forget 'em. Leave that to us, hey Li?"

I nodded absently, I couldn't even begin to think what he was on about.

"Yeah," I said, "You scat Bonk, we'll see y', like Dinny

says. Go on, scat," I snapped as he hesitated. Dinny poked his head round the door.

"Good," he said, "It's easin' off. Let's go."

"Hey Din, 'ang on a minute will y'. What the 'ell's goin' on? What're y' cookin'?"

"Easy," he said confidently. "We go t' the cemetery, nick a coupla wreaths, give 'em t' Bonk, 'e delivers 'em an' Bob's y' uncle."

I looked at him in amazement.

"Y' can't go round nickin' wreaths Din. Suppose'n we get caught? It's bad enough gerrin the poke without gerrin tangled up with the Scuffers."

"Take it easy," he said soothingly. "There's nuthin' to it. All we've gorra do is to walk in with these," he kicked the wreaths on the floor, "'ave a gander round the cemetery 'till we see a coupla good un's, then swap 'em. We're not nickin' really are we?, just straight swappin'. There's nowt wrong with that is there?"

"Yeah, but 'ow d'we gerrem out?"

"Same way we gerrem in, carry 'em."

I had to laugh. It was typical Dinny.

"OK, you're on," I said enthusiastically. "Where's the nearest cemetery?"

He thought for a moment. At our age we weren't very well up on cemeteries. At last he named one up the north end of the town.

"Suppose there's no good un's?" I asked.

"No problem," he said airily. "People snuff it every day. There's bound t' be some."

Half an hour later, soaked to the skin by a steady drizzle, we walked through the gates under the curious eyes of the lodge keeper.

"Suppose'n 'e asks what we're doin'?" I whispered as we approached him. A ghost of a smile flickered across Dinny's face.

"Tell 'im we're gonna visit y' Aunt Fanny or summat, 'e won't know will 'e?"

The question never arose as the man's silent gaze followed us down the long pathway. Within fifteen minutes we found a couple of beauties. We swapped them quickly and made our way back. The lodge keeper was still in his doorway gazing at the lowering skies.

"Hey," he said as we came abreast. My heart leapt, now we were for it.

."What's up?" asked Dinny innocently.

."What y' takin' them out for?" he asked in a puzzled tone. My tongue clove to the roof of my mouth but Dinny didn't hesitate.

"Couldn't find it."

"Y' couldn't find the grave?" asked the keeper, " 'ow was that?"

I felt my legs go weak. As sure as hell we'd be nicked. Dinny shrugged.

"Well, we're on a message, y'know, for wanna the neighbours. She was gonna come 'erself burrit was rainin so bad we said we'd come for 'er. Y'know a good turn like."

The lodge keeper grinned.

"I'll soon fix you up. Jus' gimme' 'er name an' I'll look it up in the book. Seems a pity t' come all this way then 'ave t' take 'em back."

I caught Dinny's expression out of the corner of my eye. I could almost hear his brain buzzing.

"Mrs Green," he said without batting an eye.

"Right," said the keeper. "Come in outa the rain . . . What's the address? . . . Oh yeah, What religion was she?"

"She's a Catholic."

"Is?"

"Yeah, she lives near us."

"So, 'oo were the wreaths for then?"

" 'er sister."

"Oh, that's OK. What was 'er name?"

Dinny clapped his hand to his mouth in mock surprise.

"Cor 'ell, I've forgot it." He turned to me, "Hey Li, can you remember it?"

I shook my head, "I wasn't there when she asked y' t'

39

come, remember? Y' came round for me."

"Oh yeah, I forgot. Blimey what was it?"

"The keeper laughed. "You're a bright pair aren't yeh? I'll lay ten t' one you'd forget y' 'ead if it wasn't screwed on. Anyroad I can't 'elp y' without the name." Dinny sighed disconsolately.

" 'ell," he said sincerely, "We'll 'ave t' come back Li, I 'ope this flippin' rain stops. I don't fancy this walk again d'you?"

"Ah, you'll be alright," said the keeper. "The walk won't kill y'."

"We'll be in the right place if it does," answered Dinny with a grin, "Anyroad, thanks a lot mister, see y'."

With a friendly wave we turned and walked slowly to the gate. Once out of sight we ran like the clappers.

With the wreaths delivered on time, and the recipients gasping at the quality, Bonko was safe once again. All that remained was to sort something out before I got home at the usual finishing time. We split Bonko's tip three ways, a penny each, then Dinny and I made our way to his house for a cup of tea and a rub down. As usual the place was like Bedlam. Mrs Devlin, placid as ever, sat serenely unconcerned as the kids fought and argued over their share of the bowl of stew on the bare table. She was well ahead of her time in allowing free expression, about two thousand years ahead.

Even Dinny finally got fed up.

"Ah bugger it," he said finally, "Let's go for a walk in the town. It's like a flamin' mad'ouse 'ere." I didn't argue. We grabbed a butty apiece and left them to it. Within fifteen minutes we were strolling down the main shopping centre in the pale watery sunshine, crossing and recrossing the road to gaze into the shop windows. Gradually we worked our way down until Dinny, ever curious, stopped outside a newly opened wireless shop.

"Hey Li," he said, pointing excitedly to a brand new, heavily built wireless on display. "Look at that. A beauty isn't it?"

I looked at it admiringly. The nearest we had ever got to a wireless set was when Uncle Tom's crystal set broke down and our Con fiddled with it for him. My eye caught a small notice in the corner of the window, just above Dinny's cropped head. I nudged him.

"Look at that." Dinny raised his head and looked at the notice.

'Strong boy wanted' it said. He grabbed my arm.

"Gerrin' there before some other kids see it," he snapped. I hesitated a fraction of a second. He gave me a push.

"Git," he repeated as a group of lads came strolling along.

The shop, dark, forbidding and seemingly devoid of life, smelt musty as I crossed the threshold. I stood uncertainly just inside.

"Dingle it," hissed Dinny, poking his head round the door.

"What?"

He nodded towards a small domed shaped object on the counter.

"The bell, dingle it. I'll wait outside for y'." He winked, "Don't forget, warrever 'e asks y' cin y' do, say yeah, gorrit? I'll keep tags in case these others see the notice."

Before I could reply he was gone. So, with a confidence I didn't feel, I banged the bell. A small gnome like figure slid quietly from the shadows and stood before me. Bald headed, with a pair of steel rimmed spectacles perched on a beak-like nose, his bright eyes flickered over me as he stood silently waiting for me to speak.

"What d'ye want?" he snapped in a high pitched voice as I remained silent.

"I'm strong," I announced. His bushy eyebrows raised in surprise.

"So," he said, "You're strong . . . I should be pleased?"

I was a bit non-plussed. It wasn't going as I intended.

"The notice," I said, jerking my thumb towards the window. "It says y' wanna strong boy . . . I'm strong."

He eyed me up and down with birdlike intensity as he methodically picked his yellowing teeth with a matchstick.

41

"Y' strong, OK. Can y' do shop work?"

I hadn't a clue but followed Dinny's advice.

"Course I can," I said confidently.

"Can y' lift that?" he nodded towards a large cardboard box against the end of the counter.

"Course I can," I repeated, moving towards the box and placing my hands under it. I don't know what was in it, but if I'd been wearing a jock strap it would have dropped off under the strain as I struggled with it. Legs and arms screamed with the effort, but I had to do it. It could mean the end of all my present worries. I got my foot under it, then, with a superhuman effort got it to my knees. Eyes popping I held it clear of the ground under his unblinking stare, then he nodded for me to put it down. My back creaked as I straightened and gazed anxiously at him. For ten pulsating seconds he picked his teeth in silence.

"OK" he said at last. "You've gorrit. When can y' start?"

I gazed at him open mouthed, I had *got* it.

"Now," I said eagerly, then, remembering Dad's advice, I popped the fatal question. "What time do I finish?" I trembled as he scowled.

"Y' 'aven't started yet." he said menacingly. For a terrifying second I went numb. God, I didn't want to lose it now, not with a crowd of kids already gazing into the window despite Dinny's heroic efforts to keep the notice covered.

"I only asked because me Mam'll wonder where I am," I said desperately.

He relaxed, "Yeah, I suppose she will. Alright then, six o'clock."

I felt a sense of relief. Some of the kids worked until eight or nine, and a damned sight later on a Saturday night. Six wasn't bad. Again with Dad's advice in mind I took the next hurdle.

" 'Ow much a week?"

He looked at me for several seconds rubbing his blue-black jowl.

"Four bob, an' a shillin' extra if y' work late."

I gazed at him incredulously. A rise, and I hadn't even started yet!

"Right," he said, suddenly all business, "Get them there boxes shifted inter the back." He jerked his thumb at a pile of boxes similar to the one I had lifted. I groaned inwardly as I bent down to start. "Oh yeah," he added, "Before y' start on them, shift those kids from around the door. They're blockin' trade." I hesitated. "Go," he snapped, "Shift 'em." I strode purposefully towards the door.

"Come on," I snapped to a startled Dinny, "Git, an' take that lot with y'. Y' blockin' trade."

He looked at me with open mouth then a grin creased his face.

"You've gorra bloody neck an' no mistake'. Five minutes an' y' the boss already." He turned, shooing the kids before him. I called after him in a strangled voice. "Hey Din."

"Yeah?"

"Tell me Mam will y'?" He grinned and nodded. "An' don't forget to tell 'er I'm gerrin four bob a week, *and* I'm in a shop."

He stuck his thumb up and winked. I turned and walked into what was to be a nightmare cavern, and set to with a will.

4

The Cavern

"Liam', where the devil are y'?"

Mr Golder's irritable falsetto voice pinged through the thin store room door as I struggled to lift a heavy box on to the crowded shelf above my head. I twisted round.

"In 'ere,' I squawked, desperately trying to prevent the box slipping.

"Well come outa there. It's me dinner time an' y' haven't got the tin yet."

I swore silently. For six weeks now, in the darkened cavern which seemed to close around me every time I walked through the door, I had listened to that squeaky voice. I hated it. I hated its wizened owner sitting like a predatory spider in his dark cubby hole at the end of the counter. I hated the stacked accumulators, wired in serried rows like a corner of Frankenstein's laboratory as they silently charged at sixpence a time for customers well off enough to afford the new fangled wireless sets. Twice I had received shocks from the damned things and once, in my second week, actually committed the cardinal sin of dropping one, scattering acid over the floor. He kept on about it the whole week afterwards. Above all I hated delivering the damned things. I walked miles round the town because he was too mean to get a bicycle with a basket on it, which meant that the most I could carry was four. It was an endless treadmill of a chore, with journeys doubled and trebled as the trade grew.

I wished to God I had never seen the notice in the window and it put me off shop work for life. I felt trapped, suffocated, helpless, but without another job to go to I dared not leave. It would have been disaster for Mam.

I poked my dust streaked face round the door. He waved his thin claw-like hands at me.

"On my life boy, what do I pay you good money for? Four shillings no less, an' what do I get eh?"

Nerves screaming, I stood grim faced under the tirade. Anger strained within me, I'd love to tell him what to do with his four shillings, and nearly did. I had worked like a slave since eight that morning. Sweeping, cleaning, moving stock, changing and delivering accumulators, then had watched his miser-like counting of the small heap of coins on my return. For the last hour, in near terror of dropping and breaking something, I had been trying to bring some kind of order into the darkened store room. If only he had let me put the light on, but it was daytime and light cost money.

I fought down my anger as he felt in his waistcoat pocket for the sixpence for his daily tin of sardines. No flaming wonder he was oily with the customers. He scoffed the damned things as though they were manna from heaven. In all the time I was there I never knew him to eat anything else except the sardines, a slice of brown bread, and the whole washed down with a cup of tea from the cafe next door.

"No loiterin' mind," he admonished. "I'm hungry, I don't pay y' t' stand chatterin. Five minutes, that's all." I uttered the ritual protest, "But the shop might be full . . ."

"Five minutes, otherwise . . ."

It was always the same threat, "Otherwise." He knew there were a hundred kids wandering past the shop every day of the week just clamouring for a job, *any* job. It was an invisible whip, and by God he knew how to use it, but deep down I knew that even for Mam's sake I couldn't stick it much longer, I'd either go crackers, or thump him, one or the other.

I took the proffered sixpence then, on the way out caught a glimpse of another sixpence nestling just near the window end of the counter. I ignored it. I had seen too many before to touch it. The miserable bastard was trying it on again to test my honesty. The first two or three he had put there, a favourite trick in those days to test the kids, I had picked up and handed to him, but now I let the old sod pick them up himself. It was Dinny who had put me wise to what he was up to.

"What did y' do?" he asked in alarm the first time I mentioned finding one.

"What d'y' think?" I asked indignantly. "I give it t' the boss."

"An' a bloody good job too," he said. "Ten t' one 'es testin' y'."

I was astounded, but he had been around a lot more than me so I knew he wasn't kidding.

"I've got a good mind t' tell me Dad."

"No, leave it Li, y'know y' ole man, 'ed be round there an' 'ave his flamin' liver. Just leave it, it'll serve the old sod right if someone walks in an' picks it up under 'is nose, then 'e *will* lose it for sure."

I followed his advice, but periodically throughout my stay the odd three penny or sixpenny piece turned up. The girl in the grocer's knew what I wanted and slapped the sardines on the counter as I walked in. I was back within minutes. He held his hand out for the two pence change. I put three half pence into his hand. He looked at it, then at me.

"Come on, where is it?"

"Where's what?" I asked, puzzled.

"The other half penny. Come on, 'and it over," he said menacingly.

"That's all she gave me" I said, "Sardines must've gone up or summat."

The hand remained out.

"Give," he said.

"I felt myself go cold as blind anger swept me. He was saying I had stolen it. The frustrations of weeks boiled over.

"Y' cross-eyed bastard," I yelled. "I told y', that's all she gave me. If y' don't believe me, go an' ask 'er."

46

He straightened as though I had struck him. Eyes blazing he flung the tin on the counter and made to grab me, but he had no chance. I was under his arms and behind him in a flash, fists balled ready for anything. He whirled around.

"What did y' say?" he snarled, lips quivering angrily. But I was past caring. I never even thought about it being pay day. All I knew was that he had accused me of something I hadn't done. He was fortunate that I was no bigger. In that mood I'd have done some damage. He must have sensed my determination as I snarled at him. "I'm goin' for me Dad. Y' said I pinched y' bloody half penny, an' I didn't. 'ell sort y' out mate."

He blanched and stood still for a moment. The fires in his eyes cooled.

"Now you mustn't get me wrong Liam, I didn't . . ."

"Y' said I pinched it. I told y', that's what she gave me. I never pinched nothin', I'm goin' for me Dad."

"Now Liam, think lad," he said soothingly, "If y' walk out now you'll get no pay. Just calm down now, I'll take your word fo . . ."

It was too late. His soothing words left me cold. I was hungry, dog tired, and in a flaming temper.

"I told y', I'm going for me Dad, an' y' know what y' cin do with y' sardines don't y'?" I added as a parting shot. "Y' cin stick 'em up y' jacksie!"

His mouth was still open as I left the shop, nearly taking the door off its hinges as I did so.

Ten minutes later Mam and Dad, sitting at the table drinking tea, looked up in surprise as I burst through the kitchen door.

"What the 'ell are you doin' 'ere?" asked Dad.

"Trouble," opined Mam with an experienced eye. "What y' bin doin'?"

I felt suddenly frightened. My mind went back to a few years before when I had burst in on them after Aunt Aggie had belted me. The results of that had been disastrous for both her and Mam. This time it would be Dad who took up the cudgels, and he was even more unpredictable than she was in a temper.

"Nothin'," I said, frantically trying to back pedal on my emotions.

"Pull the other one," said Dad, "Its got bells on. Come on, Whats up with y'? Y' got the sack?"

"I walked out."

"Y'what?" gasped Mam. "Did y' get paid?"

"No."

"What d'y' mean no? You've worked all week 'aven't y'? What 'appened?"

The floodgates opened.

" 'e said I diddled him outa a 'alfpenny."

"A *halfpenny*? Y' kiddin'."

"Be quiet a minute Pat," snapped Mam agitatedly. "Let 'im tell us." He glared at her, but remained silent.

"Well?" she said. I opened my mouth to speak. She glared at me menacingly. "The truth mind, no bloody nonsense or I'll wallop y'." She would too. I licked my lips nervously.

"I went for 'is sardines, 'e 'as 'em every day," I added by way of explanation. "*Every* day?" she exclaimed. I nodded. She looked at Dad. He shrugged.

" 'ell's bells!" she said with a grimace, " 'e must be on 'is uppers. Go on then."

" 'e usually gives me sixpence, an gets tuppence change. Today the girl only gave me three halfpence."

"So?" said Dad. "They must've gone up. What's up with that?"

"That's what I told 'im, but 'e wouldn't believe me."

"Why the 'ell didn't 'e go an' ask then?" queried Mam.

"That's what I said, but 'e wouldn't. 'e just kept on askin' for it an' I got mad."

"What did y' say?" I hesitated. I had dreaded this particular question. Though they swore like troopers themselves, I daren't, not in the house. I began to wish I had never come home to tell them.

"What did y' say?" she repeated slowly. "Come, the truth."

48

Still I hesitated, shifting uncomfortably from one foot to the other.

"I won't ask again," she said with a distinct edge to her voice. "I want to know everything." There was nothing else for it. In as quiet a voice as possible to lessen the shock I told them.

"I called 'im a cross-eyed bastard, an' told 'im t' stick 'is sardines up his jacksie." They looked at each other incredulously.

"Y' called 'im *what*?" asked Dad.

Anxiously watching their expressions I repeated it slowly. They seemed suspended between anger and laughter.

"Oh God," gasped Mam, as Dad put his elbows on the table and cupped his head in his hands.

"An' 'e said 'e wouldn't pay me if I came 'ome t'tell y'," I added.

Dad's eyes narrowed as he raised his head then got to his feet.

"Oh yes 'e bloody well will," he said with quiet menace.

"Where y' goin'?" I asked anxiously as he reached for his jacket and slipped it on.

"Where d'y' think" he snapped. Mam rose agitatedly.

"Pat," she said anxiously, "For God's sake don't lose y' temper. Things are bad enough without makin' them fifty times worse."

"Mind y' own business, I'll see t' this . . . come on," he snapped to me.

"Please," cried Mam. With the door half open he turned to her, grim faced.

"Look, we may be on our uppers, but nobody's gonna accuse wanna mine of pinchin', I'm gonna sort this out now."

Within ten hectic minutes, during which I told him of the sixpences left lying around, we were in the grocer's. Dad questioned the girl. Yes the sardines had gone up a halfpenny. Minutes later we were in the shop, confronting a white faced Mr Golders. Dad's behaviour was a revelation, I had expected him to go for the boss bald headed, but he didn't. With deadly calm he leaned over the counter and to the obvious approval of one interested customer, he castigated him in colourful shipyard language. He waxed particularly eloquent on the subject of leaving coins lying around and I felt a glow of satisfaction that I had chosen the right description for him. Even Dad thought he was a cross-eyed bastard and said so. It was all over in a few minutes during which my ex-boss remained completely silent until Dad held his gnarled hand out.

"His wages," he snapped. "Come on . . . Give."

"But . . ."

"Give," repeated Dad. "Or I'll step outside an' call the nearest scuffer an' see what 'e 'as t' say about false accusations."

Mr Golders put his fingers into his waistcoat pocket, then put three shillings and two sixpences on the counter. Dad pushed one of the sixpences back.

" 'e left early t'day so 'e 'asn't earned that. As 'e told y', y' cin stick that up y' jacksie with the sardines mate."

I gazed at him admiringly as we left the shop. I was free. I could have danced for sheer joy. Then I came to earth with a bump. I was also unemployed.

My despondency was short lived. In the short time we had been away my brother Con, away wandering the country in search of work for months past, had returned home. Face pinched, and as thin as a lathe, he looked awful. Mam, never one to show emotion, looked misty eyed as she sat between my eldest sister Bernadette and her fiery husband Jimmy Kiernan and watched Dad greet him affectionately.

"No luck?"

Con shrugged his shoulders despondently. "Things are worse in Wales than they are 'ere. There's thousands out there. Honest Dad, y' wouldn't believe it."

"I'll believe it Con, in fact I'll believe any bloody thing now," replied Dad as Con came towards me and put his hand on my shoulder.

"I see y' still in trouble·Li?" I grinned sheepishly. At

least Con's return would dampen the trauma of my losing my job.

"What 'appened?" he asked.

"Must've been worked t' death in that place," broke in Dad. "A right flamin' skinflint that bloke was, I'll tell y' . . . 'es better outa there."

"Where was that?" asked Con.

"Oh you won't know it. It's a new wireless shop near the market."

"I'm glad 'e's outa there" said Bernadette. "It's not 'ealthy inside."

Good old Bernadette. Despite the many surreptitious thumps she had given me over the years for being cheeky, she always stuck by me when I was in trouble.

"Look luv," snapped Jimmy. "They're lucky to get anywhere these days. It's bad enough for us, we're used to it, but what the 'ell chance've they got . . . none."

I looked across at the sallow, bitter face. Poor Jimmy, he had worked himself to the bone to avoid the unemployed riots of 1932. But for him they would have broken out a lot sooner than they did, but in the end he was swept along like everyone else in a desperate attempt to get relief from the grinding poverty that gripped them all. It hadn't done any good. Nearly four years later people were still hungry, the Means Test men still probed among families that were split wide open. He looked at Seamus, turned three now and growing like a weed, as his son tried to escape his father's grasp.

"I wonder what'll happen to these fellers when they grow up?" he muttered half to himself.

"Oh Jim," snapped my sister impatiently. "Don't start on that again, it can't go on forever."

Jimmy looked at her solemnly, "I wouldn't bet on it chuck. The likes of 'im," he nodded in my direction, "might be better off in the army, at least they'd eat regular."

I looked across at Dad. Tommy Rolfe and I had gazed at the recruiting posters for hours at the army office near the market. I fancied myself in one of the gaily coloured

51

uniforms. Tom was alright, he was Orange, his father couldn't wait to get him into uniform. But we were Catholics, there was a difference. I had never mentioned my innermost thoughts on the army to Dad, but now that it had been brought up I took a chance.

"I was thinkin' I might join up when I was . . ."

"Oh no you bloody won't," he snapped viciously. "I want no hired assassins in this house." I was shaken by the suppressed violence in his voice.

"I only said . . ."

"Don't" he replied menacingly. "Don't even *think* about it."

I looked across at Mam for support, but she was as flint eyed as Dad. I had touched hidden passions somewhere. Bernadette leapt to my aid.

"'e didn't mean it, did y' Li?" I shook my head negatively.

" 'e could do worse," broke in Jimmy. Then his face hardened in turn as Dad whirled on him like a tiger.

"Mind y' own bloody business, or you can get out too," he snapped.

As always in our family, tension leapt with devastating suddenness. Jimmy, although now accepted as one of the family, was himself a red hot Orangeman. Without warning all the trauma of their stormy courtship seemed to burst to the surface at the mention of the army. I felt a tremor of the old fears as emotions rose dangerously and scenes of past violence flickered through my mind. I seemed to have done it again. God, why couldn't I keep my big mouth shut?

It was Con, weary from his search for work, and barely inside the house an hour, who saved the situation. He held up his hands in supplication.

"Oh Dad," he said plaintively. "Not *that* again. Can't we give it a rest? I 'aven't been in the 'ouse five minutes an' it's trouble. I thought we'd all 'ad enough of that."

They looked at each other shamefaced. He turned to me.

"Look Li, I know y' don't understand these things yet, but do me a favour will y'?"

"What?"

"Don't mention the flamin' Army again while I'm 'ere will y'?"

"Why?" It was out before I could stop it.

"Why? Because y' grandad was shot on 'is own doorstep in Ireland, that's why. 'Ow d'y' think Dad feels?"

I felt terrible. I had forgotten all about the troubles that had been a rallying point for all Catholics ever since I could remember. Trust me to put my foot in it.

"Go on Li, scat," said Bernadette in the still tense atmosphere. "Everythin'll be alright don't worry. There's not gonna be no row."

I looked at her gratefully. I never wanted to see another row at home as long as I lived. The last real one, when Dad blew his top and went on a three day drunken spree, was enough to last a lifetime. That too had been caused by an almost casual remark by Mam. Frustrated beyond endurance by the continual struggle and with not a penny in her purse that particular day she thoughtlessly snapped Dad's head off with a biting remark. The words, born of desperation were simple, the results terrifying.

"Why can't y' gerra job?" she snapped and regretted it a split second later as Dad, after years of trying, suddenly blew. The house finished up in smithereens as everything movable went sailing through the air. It was Con then who had prevented murder being committed as Dad, in an ecstasy of passion at the unconscious insult, picked up a knife and threw it blindly. Thanks be to God it was the handle and not the blade that hit Con squarely between the eyes as he stepped between them and went down as though poleaxed. Dad himself vanished for three whole days, then landed home paralytic. Only the good offices and sound commonsense of Father Mac from the priest's house had finally brought the family ship back on to an even keel. It had been a close call for all of us. For one searing moment that would stay with me for ever, they had cracked under the burden. I looked anxiously from one to the other as I hesitated to go.

"Go on Li, everythin'll be alright."

"Oh," broke in Mam, as I made my way gratefully to the door. "While y' at it y' can go a message for me." I felt the tension ease as I looked at her. "Go an' tell y' Aunt Min Con's 'ome, ask 'er if she can spare some tea."

With a quick ruffle of Seamus's hair I shot through the kitchen door.

I was both glad and sorry that Con was home. Glad because he was safe and sound, and sorry because I knew I would lose my single bed and have to sleep on the sofa again in the parlour. Still, I didn't mind that really.

With my message safely delivered to a delighted Aunt Min, I made my way down to the shipyard to try and see Dinny. Halfway there I bumped into Sniffer Johnson. None of us had seen him for several days although we had heard on the grapevine that he was running with a gang of roughs. He looked pretty pleased with himself in his new Jersey.

"Hi ya, Sniff, where y' bin?"

Sniffer, he didn't get his name for nothing, twisted his mouth and inhaled deeply up his left nostril, then grinned like a Cheshire cat.

"Hi ya, Li."

"Where y' bin?" I repeated, " 'aven't seen y' down the shed lately. What y' bin doin' . . . workin'?" He let out one of his maniacal laughs.

"Workin'," he said scornfully. "What's the use of workin'? Just 'ave a gander at this." He pinched his new jersey between finger and thumb.

"Swankin' aren't y'. Where did y' gerrit?"

"Where d'y' think?" he said with a knowing wink. "Me Dad gorrit."

"Yeah?" I said sarcastically. " 'E got three months in Walton too, didn't 'e?"

I had an uneasy feeling that Sniffer was following in his Dad's footsteps. It was a well known fact that old Johnson had two fingers of the same length. Even with a handshake it was policy to count your fingers afterwards. This was his second stretch in eighteen months.

"Why 'aven't y' bin t' the shed lately?"

"None o' your business," he replied cockily. I felt a surge of anger and stuck my fist under his nose.

"Jus' watch it mate, or you'll sniff on the other flamin' side of y' nose. I asked y' what you were doin'. If you get the gang inter trouble with the scuffers you're in for it, and I'm not kiddin'."

"I'm not doin' nothin'," he answered truculently. "Anyroad, I'm not in your gang now, I've got some mates t' go around with."

"Fair enough, that's up t' you, but I warn y' don't bring trouble to us, especially 'enry." He gave a high-pitched laugh.

" 'es an 'oly Joe 'e is" he sneered. "If 'e wants t' be a priest that's 'is lookout, 'es got nuthin' t' do with me."

"Jus' watch it Sniff that's all, I'm warnin' y'. Cock 'is chances up an' I'll do y'. If you wanna finish up like y' ole man that's your business, but don't bring the scuffers on our flamin' necks, gorrit?"

"I'm not doin' nothin' t' y'. They're my mates Now, they're a great bunch, there's no flies on them I'll tell y'."

"I tell y', you're a mug mate, if the scuffers get their 'ands on y' you've 'ad it."

He looked at me in sullen silence with his big brown eyes. Suddenly I felt irritable with him. He had always been a bit crackers like his old man but basically he was a good lad and we had been friends a long time. Easily led, his new mates would drop him straight in it as sure as hell, to save their own necks if they had to. If he had been a Catholic, I could have tipped the wink to Father Mac to have a quiet word with him but, like Tommy, he was Orange, so that was out.

Even a couple of years ago while we were at school I could have belted him over the ear to bring him into line but now it was different. We were 'grown up'; if he wanted to finish up in Walton, or get the 'Cat', that was his hard luck. I had no more time left to argue. If I stayed much longer I'd miss Dinny. I made one last try.

"Look Sniff, don't be bloody daft mate. There's enough trouble around without lookin' for it." He grinned vacantly.

"Oh please y'self'," I snapped. "Y' know where the shed is, it's up t' you."

I turned abruptly and left him standing uncertainly on the kerbside.

He still occupied my mind when Dinny's familiar voice stopped me in midstride.

"Hi," he yelled down my ear. "Where y' goin'?"

I looked up at the dirt grimed face and grinned.

"Gonna meet you."

"Well 'ere I am. What's up?"

"Just seen Sniffer."

"Yeah? Where's 'e workin'? I 'aven't seen 'im for weeks."

" 'es not, 'es nickin'. Gorra new jersey on an' 'e can't afford that."

"That figures, two fingers of the same length, an' as daft as a brush like 'is ole man, 'e'll do time for sure, you'll see."

"Yeah, looks like it, the silly sod."

"Anyroad," said Dinny in a puzzled voice, "Warra you doin' 'ere? Why aren't y' workin'?" I grinned.

"Got the sack . . . well, sort of anyroad."

" 'ow come?"

"Ah, I'll tell y' in the shed later. You'll laugh."

"No I won't, I'm not comin' t'night."

"Y'what?" I gasped. He was my closest friend and rarely missed coming to the shed for a natter. It must be something serious. "Whats up?"

"Nuthin's up," he said with a grin. "Jus' gonna see a Judy, that's all."

"Not *again'*," I gasped. This was the second time he had been out with a girl. His arm was only just better after falling over Maggie's feet at the dance.

"What d'y' wanna Judy for?"

Surprise and disgust must have shown in my voice. Until Dinny's recent lapse girls had never entered our world. We just had no time for them. Anyway they scared me stiff. It was bad enough having sisters.

He bridled at my tone, and for the second time in half an hour I had the uneasy feeling that my world was changing.

Just a couple of years ago we were at school and a tight knit bunch, now everything seemed different. First Henry showing increasing signs of religion, then Tommy, all set to join up on Boy Service. Less than half an hour ago it was Sniffer, seemingly hell bent on trouble, and now Dinny, of all people talking about girls. What the hell was going on?

"Why shouldn't I go out with a Judy?" he demanded. I shrugged, there was no answer to that one.

"Who is she?" I countered.

"Freda Wilkinson, y'know?"

"Freda!" I cried scornfully. "What d'y' wanna go out with 'er for? Look," I added enticingly "I've got some grub in the shed, an' y' know Bonko always brings some fruit. Anyroad," I added as a clincher, "She's got pimples."

I felt frustrated. Dinny was both older and wiser than me, and had certainly been around a lot more. I sensed a threat to our close friendship. I tried once again to dissuade him.

"What y' gonna do with 'er anyroad?" I asked. He grinned broadly, then shrugged.

"Dunno," he said noncommittally. "Depends on 'er. It's the first time I've took 'er out."

We stopped at the corner of the entry leading to our street. I felt irritable and uneasy and momentarily wished we were all back at school, without these new distractions. His voice brought me back to the present with a jerk.

"Right, tarrar well. See y' termorrer. I'm jus' gonna grab some tea, gerra wash then we're off."

"Where y' goin'?" I asked in an effort to detain him.

"Down the *dive* I think she said."

I looked at him incredulously. The dive was a notorious cellar dance hall in one of the back streets. Its name daren't even be mentioned at home. Teresa, my youngest sister, on one of her rare visits from her servant job in Dublin, got a hiding from Dad just for being seen in its vicinity. Mam had called her a scarlet woman and Dad just walloped her, even though she was nearly twenty. Dinny was only fifteen and a half! If that was me I'd get the buckle end of the belt and no mistake. I shuddered at the risk he was taking. If that's what girls did to you then as far as I was concerned you could keep them, I'd stick to the black puddin' I had in the shed.

I watched him go with a mixture of fear and wonder, remembering with a tinge of envy that his Mam and Dad, with so many kids in the house, probably didn't even know they *had* him until pay night.

With a final wave he vanished down the entry and I turned disconsolately towards the shed, wondering what the rest of the gang was up to.

5

Faith — You're Joking

It was three days before I saw Dinny again and for the first time in weeks, the whole gang, with the exception of Sniffer, sat outside the shed in the hot July sunshine. It was just like the old days, arguing about what we were going to do for the rest of the Sunday. As usual Fatty Boyle put his foot in it.

" 'ows the Judy Din?" he asked casually. Dinny glared at him.

"Don't talk t' me about Judies," he snapped. I grinned. I had heard on the grapevine that his new venture had not gone quite as he had hoped. I winked at Fatty encouragingly. He obliged.

"I 'eard she was, well y'know. . . . Cor!"

"Shut it," snapped Dinny. "Let's get goin'." He half rose to his feet.

"No 'ang on a bit Din," I said, making myself comfortable against the warm wooden wall. "There's no rush. Tell us about the dance. What was it like?"

"Y' cin stuff dancin'," he replied darkly. "Cost me a bloody shillin' it did. A shillin' mind y', an' what for? Jiggin' about with a bag fulla pimples, *and* I finished up with a shiner." He pointed to his left eye, now turning a delicate yellow.

"What 'appened?" I asked.

"I dunno," he replied uncertainly. "I paid a tanner each t' gerrin, fell down the flamin' stairs inter the cellar an' banged me 'ead."

"Didn't they 'ave no lights?" asked Fatty.

"Y' kiddin'," replied Dinny scathingly. "They don't need

no lights for what's goin' on down there mate."

"What was they doin'?" persisted Fatty. Tommy Rolfe, a few months younger than me and already showing signs of the powerful man he was to be, laughed loudly.

"Cor Fatty, no kiddin', you're innocent an' no mistake. What d'y' think they were doin'?"

"Dancin'," replied Fatty innocently. "That's what the dive is, isn't it? A dance 'all. Anyroad Din what 'appened?"

"I told y', I fell arse over 'ead down the steps, picks meself up and grabs 'olda Freda . . . well I thought it was Freda but it was another Judy. Next thing I know I'm on the floor again with some silly sod treadin' on me."

"What did y' do?" asked Tom.

"What d'y' think I did? I lashed out with me foot."

We gasped, kicking wasn't the normal way of fighting those days. He must have felt the hostility.

"Well," he said defensively, "'e was a big feller. Anyroad I didn't kick 'im."

" 'o did y' get then?" I queried interestedly.

"Freda," he said with a grin.

"What, the Judy?" gasped Bonko.

"Yeah," replied Dinny with an air of satisfaction. "An' she didn't 'alf 'owl I'll tell y'."

"What 'appened then?" asked Bonko. Dinny scratched his head.

"Dunno really, I know she kicked me back, then some sod belted me in the eye. Next thing I knew I was grabbed by the scruff of the neck an' finished up on the deck outside. A bloody shillin' mind y', an' I didn't even gerra flamin' dance."

"Y' can't dance anyroad," said Tommy. "What did y' go for?"

"I didn't wanna go, she did," he winked. "I wanted t' go t' the park where it's quiet like, y'know?"

"I suppose y' wanted t' explore 'er pimples?" said Tommy sarcastically. Dinny grinned and winked again.

"A coupla them anyroad."

"Serves y' right," broke in Henry quietly. "That's what

60

y' get messin' about with Judies. Me Mam says most of'm are hussies anyroad."

"We can't all be priests y'know," complained Fatty. "If we were you'd 'ave nobody t' preach to would y'?"

Tommy, the only Protestant among us, sprang to Henry's defence.

"You leave 'im alone Fatty. He can't 'elp it if 'es 'oly can 'e?"

"Alright Tom, Fatty didn't mean nothin' did y'? I can stick up for meself."

He could too. That thin deceptive body, surmounted by an angelic fce, was tough and stringy through years of battling against privation like the rest of us, but I could only ever remember him in one private fight all the years I knew him. Gang fights, when we all pitched in together, yes, many a time when we were at school. But with his gentle nature, strangely out of place in the rough world around him, he seemed to be able to ease himself through every crisis with a silver tongue. I envied him in many ways and often wished that the fiery temper I had inherited from a mixture of Spanish and Irish parents could have been a little less explosive. If ever he got the chance he would make a good priest, but without a penny to bless themselves I didn't fancy his chances.

I looked at the ragged figure with its neatly combed hair. At least he knew what he wanted to be, even if he never got there, but God knows what would happen to the rest of us. The subject changed abruptly as Fatty, with his uncanny knack of putting his foot in it, spoke again.

"Hey, warrabout Sniffer then?"

I gave him a puzzled look. I had heard nothing in the three days since I had last seen him.

"Warrabout 'im?" I snapped, sitting upright.

" 'es in that gang from Frogmore Street."

"So? What else is new?"

"Well," said Fatty conspiratorially, "Y'know what they're like don't y'? They were round the Market yester-day nickin' stuff."

" 'ow d'you know?" demanded Tommy, rushing to the aid of his co-religionist.

"I saw 'em," cried Fatty indignantly, "Four of 'em. They got chased."

"Who by?"

"The market scuffers."

"Any caught?"

"Y' kiddin'," said Fatty with a grin. "They went through there like a dose'a salts."

"What were they nickin'?" I asked.

"Y'know, this an' that, anythin' they could stuff up their ganseys."

"What were you doin' there?" I demanded. "Why weren't y' at work?"

"I *was* at work, I was on a message for the boss. One'v the scuffers stopped me. The cheeky sod thought I was with 'em." Tommy burst out laughing.

" 'e mighta known you wasn't. Look at y', you'd roll quicker'n you could run."

Fatty laughed good naturedly. In the midst of universal hunger he was unfortunate to have a glandular condition that kept him permanently fat. He was used to having his leg pulled about it.

"Look," said Dinny suddenly, "Never mind all the natterin', warra we gonna do this afternoon? I'm for the docks an' a swim, whaddy y' say?"

I demurred. With plenty of ships in, the docks, our favourite spot for swimming, was oily. One mouthful of that and you'd splutter for a week.

"Warrabout the swimmin' pool then?" suggested Tommy. "It's only tuppence."

"What're we gonna do for Cozzies? I asked. "We can't swim starkers there, can we?"

None of us possessed the luxury of a swimming costume and never had.

"Look," broke in Henry, "Let's go an' 'ave a look at the tunnel."

Dinny, a man of the world, looked at him disdainfully.

The fascination of the Mersey tunnel had faded quickly after its opening the previous year.

"Y' cin stuff that Henry, who wants t' stand watchin' traffic all afternoon?"

"Yeah, suppose y' right," agreed Henry. "Not much fun in that." He turned to me.

"What d'you reckon Li?" Fatty broke in before I could speak.

"Hey," he cried enthusiastically, "I've gorra coupla lemons in the shed, warrabout the Park? The band's playin' this afternoon."

Tommy laughed, "Y'know what 'appened last time don't y'?"

We all joined in the laughter. The last time we had stood sucking lemons in front of the band, which played most Sunday afternoons in the summer, the wind section had finished up in chaos as their instruments built up with saliva and of course, we finished up being chased. We hadn't tried it since we left school.

"Great idea," said Dinny. "I could do with a bloody good laugh. Y' never know, old Twitch might be on duty."

The very thought of our favourite park keeper being on duty decided us. Minutes later, with three lemons between us, we were off.

It was a beautiful day and when we arrived the round bandstand in the centre of the park was surrounded by scores of lounging onlookers. Already in full voice was a gorgeously dressed brass band from Liverpool.

We took our places right in front of the low stand. Dinny split the lemons and passed them around, then, less than three feet from the wind instruments we stood in a silent line, sucking them. Now and then the nearest trombonist looked at us, and each time we gave him a collective slow wink as we smacked our lips on the lemons. His mate soon spotted us, then his mate. Within minutes all the wind section were emptying the surplus water out of their instruments. The more the saliva built up the quicker they had to empty them, and the tune became disjointed.

The Bandmaster, heavily built and with a long curling moustache, turned and glared at us. We sucked in silence. The inevitable happened. With the wind section desperately trying to keep up, he finally lost his temper. Red faced with anger he turned on us.

"Why don't you lot bugger off an' suck them some place else," he hissed. We carried on sucking. Sooner or later he would set the Park Keeper on to us. Another five minutes of discordant music and he did. Twitchy, leaning on the left hand side of the stand came over in response to his signal. His permanent twitch, exascerbated by emotion, became pronounced. God forgive me, I can see him now. Tall thin, and badly shellshocked in the war, this member of the Park Police must have suffered agonies through the unconscious cruelties of the children who constantly goaded him just to see him twitch.

"Wha . . . wha . . . what the bloody 'ell d . . . d . . . d'y' think y . . . y' doin'?" he stuttered, as the band emptied its instruments and started again. "Th . . . th . . . them p . . . p . . . poor bu . . . buggers up there," he indicated the sweating bandsmen, "c . . . c . . . can't b . . . blow th . . . their w . . . whatsits. W . . . w . . . why d . . . don't y' b . . . bugger off?"

"We're not doin' nothin'" said Dinny indignantly, "We're only suckin' lemons. We *like* lemons, don't we lads?"

There was a general nod of approval from the gang.

"N . . . never mind th . . . that," he said with growing exasperation. "W . . . warrabout t . . . them?"

He indicated the crowd sprawled out around us, "Th . . . they c . . . came t' listen t' the mu . . . music, n . . . not t' wa . . . watch y' suckin' b . . . bloody lemons, g . . . go on, b . . . b . . . bugger off before I n . . . ni . . . nick y'."

"It's a free country isn't it?" said Fatty indignantly, his mouth running with lemon juice. "If they can't flippin' well play that's their 'ardluck."

Twitchy looked at him savagely. Any minute now I thought, he would blow his top.

"L . . . look F . . . Fatty Arbuckle, s . . . sh . . . shut y' g

. . . gob or I'll 'ave y'." Fatty gave him a spontaneous raspberry. Twitchy made a grab for him as the band roared into action again. Next minute chaos broke out as we scattered in all directions. It was a good chase as chases go.

Poor old Twitchy, I blush with shame when I think with remorse of this gentle man we plagued so much. To us it was innocent fun. To him, who had suffered so much from the terrors of war it must have been agony. It was half an hour before we finally joined up again at the park gates and compared notes.

"Warra we gonna do now!" asked Fatty, leaning exhaustedly against the park gates.

"It's too early to go 'ome yet." I looked at Dinny. He shrugged. The others weren't certain of what they wanted to do either. I spat into my left hand.

"Right," I said, "Whichever way it goes, we'll go."

They watched as I flattened the palm of my hand containing the spittle, then, in the time honoured method of curing our indecision of where to go, I brought down my rigid right forefinger sharply on to it, the bulk shot off my palm in the direction of the docks.

"The docks it is," I said. Without argument they followed me, but it was not to be. Chattering animatedly we rounded the corner of an entry just a short distance from our church when Dinny, Tommy and myself, walking in front, were bowled over by a howling mob tearing down the narrow street.

"Jesus," yelled Dinny as he went down with Sniffer on top of him.

In sudden fury I grabbed Sniffer by the hair as I scrambled to my feet. A split second later my grip slipped as my own collar was grabbed by a powerful hand. I nearly choked as I was hauled into the air by my gansey.

"Got y' y' young sod," snarled a gruff voice in my ear. I wriggled to find myself facing Lofty Rourke, the regular beat policeman on our district. He looked at me in surprise.

"You!" he cried. "What're you doin' mixed up with this lot?"

"Y' got the wrong one Seamus," broke in his beat mate, Ely, "That's Sullivan."

"Well I'll be damned," said Lofty, straightening my collar. "I thought we 'ad 'em."

"What's goin' on?" demanded Dinny with all the force of innocence. "We've done nuthin', we're just walkin'."

"Which way did they go?" demanded Ely.

"What've they done?" I countered.

"Chuckin' bloody stones," snapped Lofty.

"Is that all?" I asked incredulously. "I thought they'd pinched the town 'all clock or summat."

"There'd be less trouble if they 'ad. Now come on, who are they?"

Whatever it was Sniffer had done, there was no way they were going to get that information out of us.

"What 'ave they done?" asked Tommy, more calmly now that our own innocence had been established.

"Just broke half a dozen winders in the church, that's all," snapped Lofty, "An' y' know what that means, so come on, you know 'em. Where are they?"

I felt a prickle of fear at the news. It was the tenth of July. With the Orangeman's Day march just two days away, it meant almost certain trouble unless they caught the culprits. I looked at Tommy, the only Protestant among us, and from a red hot Orange family. It was less than four years since the church itself had been invaded, and feelings still ran high in the district.

"Honest," said Henry, telling a black lie for all of us, "We don't know 'em."

Tommy looked at him gratefully. Like us, he knew that the crowd Sniffer was running with were born trouble makers. They thrived on it, and, with everyone else occupied fighting on Orangeman's Day they would have a free run in whipping what they could. I cursed Sniffer silently for his stupidity.

"Come on Liam, tell us," pleaded Lofty quietly, "Y'know

what y' Mam and Dad'd say."

"Never mind the soft soap Seamus," snapped Ely irritably, "Let's whip them down to the Bridewell. They'll soon tell us there." Lofty looked at him disdainfully. His mate was from the South, he didn't know the district like Lofty.

"Forget it," he replied wearily, "Let's go an' 'ave a word with Father Mac an' see what we can sort out. This lot wouldn't tell us anythin' even if they knew."

We watched silently as the two policemen turned and walked towards the crowd already gathering outside the church. All thoughts of the docks had gone. A peaceful Sunday afternoon had suddenly taken on infinite menace. As sure as God made little apples there would be trouble unless someone knocked some sense into the hot heads ready and waiting for anything to cause new riots. If I could have laid hands on Sniffer at that moment I'd have battered him. He just didn't seem to realise what his stupid actions could mean.

I looked at Tommy sympathetically. Twice a year with monotonous regularity, our deep friendship came under strain as religion took the district in its relentless grip and screwed everyone's emotions to breaking point.

"Never mind Tom," I said, putting my arm across his shoulders, "Everythin'll be alright on Tuesday, you'll see."

Henry, for once in his gentle life, put his foot straight in it.

"God's good Tom. There won't be no trouble."

Tommy nearly took his head off.

"What the 'ell's God got t' do with it?" he yelled. "It's all 'is bloody fault anyroad. If there wasn't no God there wouldn't be no trouble, would there? That's 'oo they're flamin' well fightin' about isn't it? . . . The daft sods."

Henry's normally pale face went white under the sudden venom. I felt a surge of anger as I saw the effect on him. He visibly wilted. Despite his rough upbringing he was, in many ways naive and it made me mad to see him hurt. Yet I felt sorry for Tom too. Forever caught between loyalty to us, all except himself, Catholics, and his family, strident Protestants from way back, he dreaded both the twelfth of July and the seventeenth of March, St Patrick's day, because as sure as hell there would be trouble, and everytime there was, the Rolfes were up to their necks in it. Poor Mrs Rolfe spent half the year wondering what was going to happen, and the other half trying to get over what had happened. Mr Rolfe just loved it. Tom's anger vanished as quickly as it had arisen.

"Sorry Henry," he said gently, "I didn't mean nothin'. It's not your fault, but you don't 'ave t' go t' our 'ouse, I do, an' there'll be ructions if the Papists start anythin'." He looked at Henry's miserable face solemnly, a sudden half smile twitched his lips.

"I 'ope when you're Pope you'll do somethin' about the bloody thing, I'm sick of it."

The tension broke as we all burst into laughter, but it didn't last. We had seen it all too often and as we wandered home in silence past the huddled chattering groups in the streets, we wondered yet again what would happen on the Twelfth.

The church was packed for Benediction that night, and the incense rose in an atmosphere that could be cut with a knife. Even as the congregation sang, they denied the God they so dutifully paid allegiance to by itching for a fight in his name.

Father MacCormack made herculean efforts to pour wisdom into bowed heads, but as always he was flogging a dead horse. Long years of poverty, blind religious fervour, and sheer unthinking hatred combined to overwhelm all commonsense. Any grace they gained from their prayers was dissipated in rebellious chatter as they left the church.

Three hundred yards up the road the Lodgeleaders, like Father Mac, tried desperately to calm things down before the great day that everyone had worked so hard to make a success of for the childrens' sakes.

For myself, I might as well have stayed at home. I wasn't praying and neither were the lads sitting with me. We spent the whole of the service trying to figure out a way to get Sniffer back into the gang and away from certain trouble with the Frogmore lot. But if Sunday was restless, Monday was like a twenty-four hour time bomb, and when Tuesday dawned in a blaze of glorious sunshine, the streets were rapidly filled with hundreds of silent expectant onlookers waiting for the procession to form up.

Every street within a quarter mile radius of the processional route was festooned with decorations. Every house provocatively displayed its faith with a crucifix or a picture of King William in the window.

At eight thirty, with men already taking up their positions on the route along the main street, I saw the first signs of the Orange children, dressed in their carefully hoarded finery, making their way through the narrow streets towards the assembly point. Sniffer, surrounded by his new mates, had never looked so well dressed in his life, walked past me with eyes downcast. I could have kicked him for the trouble that clawed at the air around us. A few minutes later Tommy, with his shock of dark curly hair neatly combed, dressed in his Sunday best with a brilliant Orange sash across his right shoulder, shrugged resignedly as he walked past, face set and unsmiling.

By eight forty-five the main street was jammed solid. As far as the eye could see there was one mass of people, some grim, some laughing easily as they shepherded the gaily dressed children beneath the banners, in the tense atmosphere.

On either side of the loose formations, the sashed bodyguards stood in two grim, silent lines, facing outwards and ready for anything. Ahead of us, hidden by the huge banners, I could hear the shrill sound of Fifes and an occasional drum roll as the invisible band warmed up, whilst in and out of the crowds, police, priests, nuns, and Orange leaders circulated constantly, dropping a word here, a warning there, to quieten the more restless spirits.

69

Suddenly tension stalked like a living thing as a scuffle broke out about ten yards to our left. We craned our necks as a tremor ran through the crowd, then a harsh voice, protesting violently, told us that the police had nabbed Lizzie Conlon, a good meths drinking Catholic and a born trouble maker, before she could do any harm. It was a pity in a way. She was well worth watching when she got going. During the riots I had watched no less than four policemen try for ten minutes to get her into a Black Maria.

For a few minutes the crowd surged restlessly as she was led away, then settled quickly as a knot of police, faces strained, hands on batons, edged their way towards the trouble spot. Henry nudged me.

"Ther's Gerty," he said, pointing to where a solid wedge of Catholics milled about the spot from where Lizzie had vanished. I watched the sweating dirt-streaked face with gleeful anticipation. Dirty Gerty, fat, sassy and fifty. I knew her well from my many trips to the pawnshop with my Dad's suit. If she spent as much on soap as she did on fish heads for her villainous looking cat, which accompanied her everywhere, she would have been well away, but she didn't and those who knew her well always stood upwind when talking to her.

I looked at the writhing twisted face as she glared belligerently at a huge docker less than two feet from her, flaunting a bright orange lily in his button hole.

"Why don't y' stick that up y' Jacksie?" she suggested loudly. He looked at her with a half grin as he raised his banner and stuck the pole in the carrier round his waist then pointed to her stays bulging uncontrollably through the rents in her dress.

"Watch y' don't fall outa them there stays Gerty," he said, dead pan, "Y' might go off with a bang luv, an' spoil the procession."

She raised her fist and shook it at him, but a policeman swiftly stepped in and eased her back screeching at the top of her voice. Suddenly Fatty poked me in the ribs.

"Hey Li, there's y' Dad." He pointed to a pub on the far

corner of the junction, and sure enough he was perched with a crowd of his mates on the broad window sill. I looked at his grim face and hoped to God he wouldn't do anything daft. Below him, on the edge of the pavement, another ardent Catholic, sporting a bright green hat balanced precariously on his head, taunted the nearest Orangeman to knock it off. The Town Hall clock struck the hour. Overhead a dark cloud drifted ominously across the sun and cast a momentary shadow over the gaudy procession. Seconds later it vanished and the fierce light glinted on the gaily painted banners. I looked for Tommy and Sniffer in the young people's section. Sniffer was missing but Tommy was right behind the band, a dangerous place if anything started. The band was always the first to be attacked. I felt a sudden pang of remorse. It all looked so lovely, too lovely for senseless destruction.

At last all was ready. I felt the tension mount in the assembled Catholics round me as last minute instructions swept the ranks. The little ones, all unaware of the frightening dangers around them, laughed and cried in excitement. On either side furtive hands among the onlookers reached into pockets filled with missiles ready for the first strident notes of the traditional music, *Liverpool Bay*.

The whole street teetered as the seconds dropped away. Bodyguards tensed for the onslaught as agitated priests and march officials renewed their efforts to calm their flocks. The Drum Major's staff glinted as he raised it high overhead. I screwed my body for the holocaust, then the police played a magnificent ace. A massive force in blue appeared as though by magic from the side streets near the head of the procession, then, splitting in two they took up position down either side. There was a gasp of astonishment from the crowd. Angry murmurs rippled like fire. Then the air was filled with missiles. Banana skins, orange peel, rotten apples and an occasional brick flew like hail. Children screamed, parents became grim faced, but the police and procession held firm. For ten agonising seconds the scene hovered between order and chaos as the stoical police suffered in absolute silence under the stern eyes of their sergeants. One false move, one word of retaliation from either side would have sparked a riot in which scores of children would have been trampled underfoot. Then, with the fickleness of all mobs, the situation changed with dramatic suddenness. From imminent conflict the mood changed to hysterical abuse as the Chief Constable played his final card and two Black Marias took up station fore and aft of the column.

Disaster had been averted, and amid the most decorative abuse, the heavily guarded procession moved off on its danger-fraught journey around the town. I felt a strange mixture of gladness and sorrow as the shrill squeal of Fifes crashed on the air. At fifteen and a half I was still only half civilised.

6

Unlikely Saviour

Christmas 1935, and what a helluva Christmas it was! The fifteenth in a row that Dad, and many like him, had been out of work. Even I, cheap labour though I was at that age, had to be content with anything I could grab after my outburst over the sardines. Con, jubilant with the labourer's job he had picked up three weeks before the holiday, found himself out on his ear just a few days before Christmas. Still, despite the appalling weather, we were all healthy, and although family presents were at a bare, home-made minimum, we had a damned good dinner on the day, which was a lot more than many of those around us had, so we were lucky.

The present I wanted above all still eluded me, a regular job, but I did manage to get taken on at the butcher's for the last two days of the rush which brought a much needed two and sixpence and a piece of meat. Actually the night I was looking forward to most was not Christmas but New Year's Eve. This was to be a special one for me, because for the first time I would be allowed to take part in the festivities instead of freezing as I sat and watched it through the stair rails.

I knew the ritual by heart of course, but to take part . . . well.

The kitchen and parlour were packed as usual. Aunt Min, round and jolly, and surprisingly still awake, sat jammed like a Toby Jug between Uncle Mat and Aunt Sarah. Con, with his new mate, stood next to me by the kitchen door ready to officiate. Mrs Taylor from next door, usually more in our house than her own, snugged her ample buttocks on the edge of the table near the parlour door, giving *The Wearing of the Green* absolute hell. Mam, smart in the new pinny given to her by a lady she took in washing for, and with her greying hair pulled tight into a bun at the back, stood near the stove waiting for the kettle to boil for the tenth time to make tea. On the mantelpiece just to her left stood the most important items of the night. A new piece of bread, a piece of coal, and a shining three penny piece. To one side of them, still wrapped in brown paper, lay the piece of bread and coal from last year. All it needed now was the witching hour itself. I looked impatiently at the clock. Nearly five minutes to midnight. Any minute now Mam would warn Dad to be ready. She was an absolute stickler for time on New Year's Eve. Even now, fifty years later, as I carry on the ritual, I can hear her voice clearly as I check the time myself.

"Pat, it's five to go. Get ready."

Quite frankly, looking back at those times, I don't know why the hell they bothered. Each year seemed a damned sight worse than the last, but there they were as usual, chattering fifty to the dozen as they sipped the precious drinks that Uncle Mat, the wealthiest among us with his permanent job at the mills, had thoughtfully provided.

Even the floods of tears that would follow the letting in of the New Year as they toasted the relatives who had come to the end of their struggles, did not put me off as my eye flickered between Mam and the clock. Bang on time she gave her warning. Dad, as the darkest person there, took the bread and coal in one hand, the three-penny piece in the other to ensure that we would not be without food, warmth and money in the coming year, Con held the door latch ready.

A deathly silence fell as the hand of the clock moved around.

"It's twelve" cried Aunt Min, "Off with yiz," Nobody moved. The clock must have been a bit fast, the Town Hall hadn't struck. Seconds later it did. Dad was out of the door like a greyhound out of a trap.

Assuming that there were no obstacles in his path, he would race down the back yard taking the old year with him. Up the narrow entry, round the top of the street and back through the front door bringing the New Year with him to a chorus of, 'Many of 'em's! Until his re-entry no one would be allowed through the front door. It would be bad luck. I don't know who the hell kept getting in before him, but as far as I could remember it had never been anything else but bad luck.

The ritual would not be complete, nor a drink taken until Dad solemnly took the old bread, opened the back door and broke it up for the birds, had taken the coal and burnt it, then with equal solemnity wrap the new offerings in paper to ensure our safety for the new year. The three-penny piece never changed, for the very simple reason it was very often the only one we had, and even in the worst times that was never spent. Without it, we would, in the true sense, be flat broke, with it we could always say we were never completely broke.

He must have been halfway through his gallop when a thunderous knocking sounded on the front door.

"It's me Dad," shouted Con.

" 'e's not that bloody quick," replied Mam scathingly, "Go an' see 'oo it is. Whoever it is don't lerrem in warrever y' do." Con dashed through the parlour door.

"Quit y' flamin' 'ammerin'." he yelled, "Y' can't come in 'ooever y' are."

"Is y' Dad in?" yelled a voice.

"Well 'e is an' 'e isn't."

"Whaddy y' mean? Is 'e or isn't 'e?"

"Yeah," shouted Con, "At least 'e will be."

"Jesus . . . This *is* Pat Sullivan's 'ouse isn't it?"

"Yes . . . 'oos that?"

" 'oo is it Con?" yelled Mam above the noise in the kitchen.

"Dunno . . . it's someone outside." Aunt Min took a fit of laughing.

"I know 'es flamin' well outside," cried Mam exasperatedly, "If 'e wasn't I wouldn't be askin' would I?"

75

" 'oo is it?" shouted Con desperately.

"It's me," yelled back an irate voice, "Are y' gonna let me in or not?"

"No, not 'til me Dad gets back."

"Well were the 'ell is 'e?"

"Runnin' round the entry."

"y'what?"

The incredulous voice outside was drowned as another thunderous knock shook the door.

"Y' can't come in," shouted Con . . . "I told y'."

"Open the flamin' door y' eejit, it's me."

He must have leaned on it as Con opened it. The house erupted as he came crashing in on all fours. He staggered to his feet breathless and made for the back door to break the bread and the stranger who followed Con in was ignored as he leaned against the door, bowler hat in hand, gazing at the scene around him.

Twice I tried to catch Dad's attention as the drinks went round and backs were thumped in good wishes. "Dad," I roared. This time I caught his attention and pointed to the beaming stranger. For a split second Dad's mouth hung open in surprise, then, beaming with pleasure he shouldered his way through with hand outstretched.

"Well I'll go t' our bloody 'ouse," he said as they shook hands. "I thought you'd snuffed it down South?"

"The stranger laughed as he took a proffered drink from Uncle Mat. Dad turned and yelled to Mam.

"Hey Mary, look 'oos 'ere." She came across and smilingly shook hands.

"Make y'self at 'ome," she said with a laugh, "Another one won't 'urt."

Gradually the chatter died away as all eyes turned to the newcomer, Dad introduced him and satisfied my curiosity.

"Ernie Ford, one'f me old shipmates.

"Warry y' doin' 'ere Ern?"

"Workin' down the Yard . . . Foreman in the Platers shop."

"Y'not?" Mr Ford nodded.

"Yep, started last week."

"What the 'ell brought y' back up 'ere for God's sake, its as rough as a bears arse round 'ere y'know."

"I know, I've 'eard all about it, but I got fixed up before I came. Anyroad I 'ad no option, the missus couldn't stick it there so I decided to pack it in."

"Well, so long as your fixed up y' alright. I wish t' Christ I was."

Mr Ford laughed. "What d'y' think I'm 'ere for?" Dad looked at him non-plussed.

"Well," said Mr Ford amid a dead silence, "D'y' want a job or not?"

"Look Ernie, don't kid me on stuff like that."

"Did I ever kid y'?"

"No."

"Well why the 'ell should I start now then? If y' wanna job you've gorrit."

The house exploded with delighted cries. I didn't know whether Mam was going to laugh or cry. It was incredible. From the moment I could remember it had been one long struggle for her to keep food on the table, and now, out of the blue, a stranger walks in, and with a few words, completely changes our lives. From that moment the hard times began quietly and gently to recede. Mam's nightmare was over. As always she was right, 'It wasn't what y' knew in this world' she said, 'It was who y' knew that counted'.

There were no tears that night, not even when they toasted those who had gone before us. I can see them now as I write, jigging and dancing to the screech of an old concertina. The house rocked, and God, alias Ernie Ford, doffed his bowler and joined in with a will. It was many weeks before I finally got the full details on him. Long, long, before I was born he and Dad had sailed the world together until Mam and Dad met and he stayed ashore. Ernie went South and fell on his feet. Dad stayed North and fell on his face.

From the moment he started work on the following Monday he was a changed man. Within two months Con had followed him into the Yard, and within six I too was in. I can remember my first day in the Yard as though it were yesterday. Dinny, already hardened to the life, was delighted when I joined him, but echoed Dad's words of the previous night as we walked together through the iron gates.

"Y' on yer own 'ere Li. Sooner or later some fly bugger 'll goad y', then it'll be up to you. Back down from a fight an' they'll run the arse of y'."

"Oh no they flamin' well won't," I said emphatically.

"Oh yes they bloody well will," he replied with equal emphasis. "Anyroad, just remember, if y' gonna fight, don't argue, 'it 'em first an' 'it 'em 'ard mate."

I knew what it was all about. It would be no good yelling for Dad or Con, they wouldn't interfere. As in the streets I had to make my own way or get to hell out of it. By lunch time on the second day I was put to the test.

The job of 'Hotting Lad' has, I believe now gone. Although new on the job I understood it well because both Con and Dad had practised me in the skills for hours at home, from the moment they knew I had been taken on. With six cold rivets, an old drum to act as a fire, and a catching funnel especially brought home for the purpose, they initiated me into its intricacies.

With a pair of long handled iron tongs to complete the outfit we practised long and hard in the backyard with Dad as the critical coach.

Twice he clipped me over the ear as Con called for a rivet and I picked and threw the wrong one, but by the end of the second session I knew it was the rivet in the centre of the ring of five that had to be thrown when called for because it was the one at the right temperature. This was immediately replaced by the next hottest rivet as they were rotated round the now empty centre. Immediately they had been rotated, a new cold rivet was placed in the empty space left in the ring, gently heating until its turn came to go into the centre for final heating before being thrown.

It was absolutely essential that strict order was maintained so that when the Riveter called, the centre one was white hot for him to work in the few seconds between his calling, to catch it, slip it through the pre-drilled holes in the ship's plates, then, with his mate on the inside of the ship, flatten it with their pneumatic drills before it cooled. They were lucky. Just before I was born the riveters still flattened them with hammers.

After the 'Knocker up' roused us on my first morning I felt quite cocky as I eagerly awaited the moment when all three of us could walk down the darkened street together.

" 'oo's 'e with?" asked Con as we rounded the corner into the main street.

"Jacky Watkins," answered Dad.

" 'ell," said Con, " 'es a buggeroo that one, 'oo's 'is mate?" Dad laughed.

"Pat Walsh. They make a right pair I'll tell y'. Spend 'alf their flamin' time arg'in with one another." I looked across at the amused faces in the growing light.

"What d'y' mean?" I asked.

"You'll find out," said Con. "Jus' remember, when Jacky calls for a rivet, lerr'im 'ave it, fast and straight. If y' miss 'ell 'ave y' liver. If that's not through the 'ole within ten seconds of 'im callin' you'll 'ave Pat out after y' too."

I looked from one to the other but there was no sign of humour on their faces. I began to worry. All my life I had heard about the 'Yard', but didn't really know it except for the rare occasions Dad had had a few days work and I had taken his dinner down in a basin. It terrified me then and I didn't feel too rosy now at the sound of my new mates.

"What's 'e like?" I asked a little nervously.

"Who?" said Dad as we headed for the gates.

"Mr Watkins, the feller I've gorra work with."

"Ah 'es alright . . . a bit crackers when 'es pushed, but 'es alright, don't worry."

"Warrabout the other feller' what's 'is name?"

"Pat Walsh, the 'older up?" Con burst out laughing. "A right nutter Pat, I'll tell y' . . . especially if y' late with the rivet."

I ignored the remark, he was obviously pulling my leg, but I was puzzled. I had heard the term 'Holder up' countless times, but what they actually did was a bit of a mystery. I tried to clear it up.

"Hey Dad, what *is* an 'Older up'?"

"Well 'e 'olds it up doesn't 'e?"

" 'olds what up?" Dad looked at me disgustedly.

"What the 'ell d'y' think?" he snapped, "The flamin' rivet of course."

The arrival of Dinny as we turned into the Yard stopped me asking any more dangerous questions. Anyway, I would soon find out.

"Hi ya Mr Sullivan."

"Hi ya Din." replied Dad as Dinny fell into step alongside, " 'ow's y' Dad?"

Dinny grimaced, "Ah y'know me Dad, daft as ever."

"An' y' Mam?" Dinny laughed.

"Y'know what she's like, easy come, easy go. Take a bloody bomb t' shift 'er."

Con and Dad laughed. They knew Fanny Devlin alright. Fat and placid she lolled through life surrounded by ten raucous kids of whom Dinny was the eldest. She was way ahead of Freud and a staunch believer in free expression, mainly because she was too damned idle to do anything about it. In any case there was not much they could damage, the whole of the front room only contained two hard backed chairs, a battered horsehair armchair upon which she was permanently enthroned during daylighthours, and a square hardwood table upon which the younger children continually etched their names for posterity. It was a simple life with all meals taken in transit. But Dinny was wrong about his Dad. He was as crafty as a bag of monkeys. When it came to getting something for nothing, he never missed a trick, and Dinny took after him. Whatever happened to him he always bounced straight back to his feet. The gang owed him everything.

"Look out for 'im Din. Show 'im the ropes will y', y' know warr'it's like?" said Dad.

"Don't worry Mr Sullivan. Li cin take care of himself, can't y' Li?"

"You betcha," I said confidently.

"Well if y' do get inter trouble," said Dad quietly, "Don't come 'ollerin' t' me. Just watch y' temper that's all." I felt peeved at the warning but the reply trembling on my lips never came as a new voice broke into the conversation.

"I see you've got the young'un with y' Pat. Is 'e down the Yard now?"

I looked up at the tall rangy figure of Mr Dillon, from the top of our street.

"Aye worse luck," answered Dad to my surprise. I thought he was pleased I was working in the Yard.

"'es lucky t'be workin' at all," grunted Con truculently. "We all are, after what we've 'ad."

"Aye, y' right I suppose," replied Dad, "But I wish t' God 'e coulda got sommat else, t'keep out this place."

I looked from one to the other in complete surprise, I always thought they liked the Yard. God knows they had spent enough weary years trying to get work in it. Of course it is as clear as crystal now but then, it left me a little uneasy. Any questions which I might have had on this new mystery was cut short by the strident blast of the Yard hooter as it warned that there was just five minutes to go before clocking on time. There was a concerted rush for the gates. Even a few minutes late could mean the loss of a quarter of an hour's pay, and for a man who lost several quarters, there was always a hundred men waiting outside the gates to take his place when he got the bullet. Within two hours I found that one was even timed going to the lavatory. If you happened to be constipated it was just your hard luck. No wonder Beechams pills were solid favourites at the time, you daren't linger.

"Tell Jacky 'es 'ad some practice, Din," said Dad as we parted just inside the Yard, " 'e'll understand . . . an' don't forget," he added, turning to me with a warning waggle of his finger, "No bloody nonsense me'lad, understand?"

Minutes later Dinny and I stood under the towering skeletal monster I was to work on. I gazed at it in awe. It looked like a gigantic spider's web of girders, planks, wires and air hoses all tangled into an inextricable mass and held together by seried ranks of plank walkways joined together by wide wooden ladders rising dizzily to a height of seventy or eighty feet above my head.

Here and there, like scruffy acolytes, Hotting lads, perched on the dangerous wooden highways, were already nursing their coke fires into life from the tiny bags of coke at their feet.

" 'ell's bells!" I ejaculated. "That's a bloody long way up isn't it?" Dinny laughed.

"Aye," he said with a grin, "An' y' don't flamin' bounce when y' fall either."

A voice immediately behind us cut off my reply.

"Hey Devlin," it roared above the noise as the Yard came to life, "Is that Sullivan?"

I turned to see a thick set man, with a face like a relief map, glaring at us. Wisps of fiery red hair peeped from beneath his filthy cap like spies as his bright blue eyes scrutinised me.

"Yeah," replied Dinny.

"Jesus!" said Mr Watkins, my new boss, "There's not much of 'im is there?"

"Don't worry Jacky 'es alright, anyroad," he added, turning to a nearby ladder, "I'm off before me mate comes lookin' for me. . . . See y' dinner time Li."

Before I could reply another voice blasted my ears.

"Hey Jacky," it roared from just behind and above me, "D'y' know what time it is mate? What's 'appened t' the bloody fire?"

I turned and looked at the huge form materialising from inside the ship on to the plank walk above me head. With a pair of beautiful cauliflower ears, he looked as if a truck had run over him.

"What the 'ell's up with you?" demanded Mr Watkins, " 'oo d'y' think 'e is? Moses with 'is burnin' bloody bush or summat? . . . 'es only just come, 'old y' 'orses."

Pat Walsh looked down at me disgustedly.

"By the look of 'im it'll take 'im all 'is time t' chuck a fit never mind a flamin' rivet."

"Me dad's bin practisin' me," I snapped indignantly. "Don't worry, I'll chuck 'em."

"Alright," broke in Mr Walsh as Pat's face darkened, "Don't be so bloody cheeky. Just gerrup there an' get the fire goin', we'll get the gear ready. Jus' give us a nod when the first one's ready. . . . Oh," he added as I turned for the ladder, "No arsin' about or you'll be out, gorrit?" I got it. Suddenly I felt nervous in this strange new world, but for seven and sixpence a week I'd master it if it killed me. With mixed feelings I made my way to the three-legged portable fire awaiting me on the plankwalk about twenty feet up the ship's side. Dad's instructions rattled round my head every foot of the way. "Stick a birra paraffin on it, not too much. Give it a birra air from the hose, not too much. When it's red in the middle, riddle it an' gerrit level, then stick y' rivets in . . . d'y' remember 'ow they go?" Oh yes, I knew how they went alright. What d'y' do then? . . . Easy, rotate them clockwise. Which one d'y' throw first. Easy again, the middle one. On my last practice I still had a question. "What would happen if I threw a cold one?" "Don't," was all he said.

My confidence vanished as I reached the fire and started the operation. Everything went wrong. I put too much paraffin on, gave it too much air, and as I flung the match in the whole flaming thing went 'whoosh' and singed my hair. Panic-stricken I got it under control amid a terrifying cacophony as the Yard swung into action. Then, singed and palpitating, I reverently placed the rivets in. They quickly hotted up.

"Rivet," roared Jacky before I was fully ready. My mind went blank and the throwing tongs stayed at my feet as I stared dumbly at Mr Walsh squatting about twelve feet away, catching funnel in his hand, pneumatic hammer on his knees ready to flatten the rivet head. For a timeless second we gazed at each other. Suddenly he blew.

"For Christ's sake lad, throw it will y'? Warry y' tryin' t' do? 'atch the bloody thing?"

A split second later Pat's voice crashed from inside the ship as he waited for the rivet to come through the plate so that he could hold it with his hammer as both men flattened the rivet to grip the ship's plates together.

"What the 'ell's goin' on out there? Where's the flamin' rivet got to?"

With both men waiting impatiently I grabbed the tongs, jabbed at the rivet and slung it blindly. Mr Walsh ducked as it whizzed past his head, clanged against the ship's side, then arched downwards like a firework.

"Below," he shouted desperately to warn anyone unfortunate enough to be in it's path. There was a wild melee below as men scattered instinctively to the warning.

"What the 'ell's goin' on up there?" yelled an irate voice. "Y' silly bugger, y' coulda killed someone."

Mr Watkins leaned over the planking.

"Ah shurrup will y'? It didn't 'it nobody did it?"

"No flamin' thanks t' you," yelled back the voice. "Jus' watch it that's all mate."

I stared in disbelief at the havoc I had caused, then Mr Watkins sarcastic voice hit me like a bullet.

"Didn't y' Dad tell y'? Y' supposed t' chuck 'em to me, not at me?" I shrank with embarrassment. "Right," he continued, "Let's 'ave another one an' this time, take y'time."

I followed his advice and felt a glow of satisfaction as the rivet went plumb into the catching funnel from where it was expertly plucked out, rammed into the hole and flattened from both sides as he and Pat hammered it in unison.

From ten feet above me a thin, boyish voice floated down sarcastically.

"What's up mate? Y' cockeyed or summat?"

Eyes flashing with temper I looked up at the grinning, grime covered face peering over the planking. I curled my fist and shook it at him.

"Watch it mate," I snarled, "Jus' bloody watch it or you'll get this down y' gullet."

He came right to the edge of the planking, cap awry, face grimacing in anger.

"You an' 'oose bloody army?" he asked.

Humiliated by my errors I was delighted to have a focal point of my own age. My foot was already on the bottom rung of the ladder leading to him when Mr Watkin's voice stopped me in my tracks.

"Hey you," he roared, "Knock it off. Any more bloody nonsense an' I'll 'ave y' round t' y' Dad."

I froze at the threat and poked at the fire viciously. Seconds later a cold rivet thumped into the plank at my feet. I looked up at the grinning face. It was a challenge. Less than half an hour into the Yard and already I was in trouble, but it was to be three full days before it broke.

I concentrated like mad and for an hour things gradually improved, then disaster struck again. I ran out of coke! Panic-stricken for the second time as the fire died, I made the cardinal mistake of throwing a rivet that was nowhere near hot enough. Both my mates castigated me. Ears tingling, I hurled myself down the ladder to the nearby coke stack, filled the bag and nearly ruptured myself as I staggered back up the ladder to catch the fire before it finally died. In a homicidal fury I looked up as my tormentor made the most of my predicament.

"What's up Lai?" he called, leaning over the edge with a grin on his face, "Y' run outa coke? . . . Aaah, poor old sod, 'ere, this'll keep y' goin'." A single piece of coke clumped onto the plank beside me. Every nerve in my body screamed at me to get up the ladder and belt him. I daren't, but I made a silent vow to have the sod sooner or later.

Dinny took one look at me as the hooter went for dinner time.

"What the 'ell's up with you?" he asked, "Someone takin' the Micky?"

"Don't you flamin' well start," I snapped, "I've got

85

enough with that bastard up there." I jerked my thumb upwards.

"Ah take no notice," he advised, "The Yard's fulla comedians. Come on let's go'n see y' Dad."

Five minutes later, still seething, we walked into the Plater's shop where Dad, Con and the rest had a card school going.

"Hi ya?" said Dad, flicking his eyes from the cards he was holding, " 'ow did y' gerron?"

"Alright," I muttered as I sat down beside Con.

"Looks like it," said my brother knowingly. "What's up?, Jacky been on to y'?"

"It's nuthin'," I snapped. Eyes narrowing, Dad looked up.

"Watch y' tongue," he said quietly, " 'e asked y' a civil question. Now what's up with y'?"

"Ah leave 'im alone Pat," advised one of his mates sitting opposite me, " 'es still wet behind the ears, 'ell settle. It's probably the lads pullin' 'is leg."

"Don't worry Mr Sullivan, I'll look out for 'im, 'ell be al . . ."

I nearly snapped Dinny's head off.

"I don't need anyone t' look after me, I cin look after meself."

Dad looked at me solemnly. "You'll 'ave to'." he said quietly.

I felt that there was a rough time ahead of me. I was right, there was.

Wednesday started bad and finished a damned sight worse. Dinny's news of Sniffer as we walked through the gate was bad. The previous night whilst the lads and I had been playing Pontoon for matchsticks in the shed, Sniffer, and two of his mates were down the Dock Road looking for drunks to roll, and Sniffer, their lookout, had been caught. According to Dinny it had all been very simple. The scuffle had alerted a couple of patrolling police. Sniffer saw them coming, yelled to his mates busily stripping a drunken sailor of his hard earned cash. It was all over in minutes. The police, whistles screeching, had nabbed them cold and the whole lot finished up in the Bridewell.

" 'ell get the Cat for sure," opined Dinny, " 'es got a record an' they'll 'ave 'im as sure as 'ell."

"No," said Dad, " 'es too young, but make no mistake, they'll birch 'im, an' serves 'im bloody well right," he added unfeelingly. "Do 'im good."

I felt myself go cold inside.

" 'ow about the others?" asked Dinny.

"If they're 'oo I think they are," broke in Con, "Then they're for the 'igh jump proper."

"Whaddy y' mean?" I asked as we turned into the Yard gate.

"The Cat," he said, "They'll get that for sure. Y'know what 'appened to the 'igh Rip gang don't y'?"

I had heard about this vicious gang of footpads some years before who had made a specialty of rolling drunks. Judge Franklin had snuffed them out like a candle in no time flat. They caught one. He sentenced him to the Cat, and warned that the next one caught would have the sentence doubled. That was enough, they only caught one more. The gang vanished like a snowdrop in hell. Like all bullies, they were about as tough as pigs' muck and twice as sloppy. Whichever way it went it was bad news about Sniffer. Idiot though he was we still felt somehow responsible for him. Thank God he was too young for the Cat, but I shuddered to think of the Birch landing on his bare backside.

We said 'Tarra' to Dad and Con, in sombre mood. I was still thinking of Sniffer when we reached the bottom of the ladders. My tormentor stood there in the half light grinning provocatively.

"Hi ya rooky," he said sarcastically, "Gorrany cold rivets y' don't want?"

Dinny looked at me. Dad's sound advice flashed through my mind.

"If y' gonna fight," he had told me, "Don't arse about, 'it first an' 'it 'ard'. All my pent emotion exploded in a burst of blind fury. One moment the grinning face taunted me, the next there was a silent crumpled heap at the foot of the ladder from a vicious blow in the solar plexus.

"Jesus'," gasped Dinny admiringly, "Y' won't get no more cold rivets off 'im."

I felt a surge of relief as I stepped unfeelingly over the crumpled form and made my way up the ladder. I felt no shame, no remorse. The bastard had asked for it. I had stood on my own two feet as I had been taught to do. I was my own man.

7

The Hot Seat

A great deal had happened in the eighteen months since I had left school. At home, through the miraculous intervention of Ernie Ford, a most unlikely saviour, we were better off beyond our dreams. With everyone working, the total income of just under a fiver made the difference between heaven and hell, and if God used Ernie as his messenger, that was his business, he got no arguments from us, but I wished he could have helped a few more around us. They were on their uppers too.

With several hundred kids waiting to grab my job if I failed, I very quickly became a dab hand with the rivets, and the two fights I had in the first three weeks ensured that the last of the Sullivans was allowed to live in peace during working hours. At home it was even better. The worry lines that had prematurely aged Mam had faded a little, to reveal a gentleness within her that I never knew existed. Dad, despite more money in his pocket, no longer headed for the pub to escape from himself but spent more and more time with his head in a book. Even Con, in regular work at last, seemed to blossom, yet despite it all I was uneasy. Something was wrong, not at home but in the gang.

I felt it as I glanced round the shed just a couple of weeks before Easter 1936. They were all there except Tom, who was still working, and Sniffer, who had opted to join the bully boys and had paid dearly for it with a dose of the birch.

They all looked the same, they talked the same, but somehow they weren't the same. For eight or nine years now we had been inseparable, sharing fun and disaster with equal imperturbability. Now, there was change in the air. Sniffer was gone, Henry, despite all the odds and through the generosity of the Bishop's fund, was already committed to the first steps in his ambition to be a priest and would soon be leaving us, as would Tommy, at last awaiting the call to Boy Service in his beloved Army. Even the town was changing I thought savagely. It just didn't seem possible that the new tunnel could have been opened nearly a year ago, yet it had. The town, I remember, had been en fête on the great day, but it had all been cosmetic, nothing had altered. Under the gaiety of the bunting the people were still hungry, unemployed and still walked the streets or hung around corners, wondering where the next meal was coming from. Even the thrill of seeing the King and Queen, sitting like a couple of highly decorated dolls on the platform, had worn thin when we were chased from the lamp-posts as we craned to see them. Still I suppose you couldn't blame the officials, there had been enough trouble on the Twelfth with the near riot of the Orangeman's march just a few days before. They didn't want anything else to go wrong. I suppose Fatty put the whole thing in a nut shell as we gathered disappointedly after being chased.

"Stuff the Tunnel," he had said viciously, "Stuff the lot'. Let's go down t' the docks."

"Hey Li'," Fatty's plaintive voice brought me back to earth, "What's up with y'?"

I looked across at him irritably.

"I was thinkin'." I snapped.

"Wharrabout?"

"Ah shurrup."

"Oh be like that then. I was only gonna ask what we were gonna do this afternoon."

"What the 'ells up with you?" asked Dinny, idly flicking a pack of cards in his hands, " 'e only asked." I looked across at Fatty's round serious face and felt a tinge of remorse. Poor old Fatty. If ever anyone was born to put

90

his foot in things it was him. It was partly the fact that he had just got the sack for the third time that had put me in a bad mood. I held out an olive branch.

"Sorry Fat, I was wonderin' what the 'ell we were gonna do about you, but don't worry, you'll soon get somethin'."

He cheered up at once and made me feel even more guilty. Where the hell was I going to find him another job before Monday?

"What did y' Mam say when y' told 'er," I asked. He shrugged.

"Cried . . . As usual."

"An' y' Dad?"

"Belted me," he said in the same flat tone. "Said I was a daft sod," he added solemnly.

Dinny burst out laughing.

" 'es not far out either. Y' gorra be daft t' throw a cabbage at the boss aint y'?"

"I didn't throw it at the boss, I threw it at Jonsey, the other lad."

"Aye," broke in Henry quietly, "But you hit the boss didn't y'?"

Fatty shrugged resignedly. "Yeah," he agreed, "But fancy sackin' a bloke for that hey?"

"Wharrabout the Yard?" asked Dinny out of the blue. "Wanna the lads off our ship 'urt 'iself on Friday so 'es knackered. Remember Li?" I nodded. Dinny had told me that one of the lads doing general helping work had fallen and hurt himself. It was a possibility, although I didn't fancy Fatty in the Yard. He was too damned awkward for his own safety. Still, it would be a job, and it would be a bit more money than he had been getting.

"Why don't y' try on Monday," I suggested. Fatty beamed.

"Y' not kiddin' are y'?" he asked anxiously.

"Would I kid y' about a job? You come with us on Monday an' see what 'appens. You've got nuthin' t' lose 'ave y'?"

"Right then we'll . . ." Dinny stopped in mid sentence

as Tommy arrived, pushing a familiar figure before him.

"Well I'll go t' our bloody 'ouse!" exclaimed Dinny, "Look what the cat's dragged in."

All eyes turned to a downcast Sniffer.

"Hi ya," he muttered, for once looking miserable.

"What brings you in?" I asked bluntly, "Where's y' mates?"

"Sod 'em," he replied vehemently.

"Where did y' find 'im?" asked Fatty.

"Moochin' about outside," said Tommy, "I told 'im t' gerrin'."

I felt uneasy with Sniffer amongst us again. He was on the police books and I didn't want the Scuffers nosing around us.

"'ows y' arse?" asked Fatty bluntly. Sniffer went crimson then white in turn.

"Bloody sore," he answered, feeling his backside.

"Serves y' flamin' well right," I said unfeelingly. "We warned y' didn't we?"

"Yeah," added Dinny, "We said the next time you'd get the Birch. You asked for it mate an' y' gorrit."

Henry, due to leave us in less than ten days time for the Catholic College at Usher Hall, spoke quietly from his seat in the corner.

"Leave 'im be Li. 'es had 'is punishment, don't rub it in."

I looked at the pale oval face with its luminous blue eyes, and the bitter retort died on my lips, but Tommy took up the cudgels.

"It's alright f' you Henry. You're off t' be a priest. Warrabout me? If the Scuffers start sniffin' around 'ere mate because of 'im, it'll likely ditch me for the Army."

I suddenly felt angry, it was never like this in the old days when we were at school. I decided to show them who was still boss.

"Stow it," I snapped, as Sniffer shifted uncomfortably from one foot to the other, 'enry's right. He's taken 'is stick, so leave it. Siddown Sniff."

He sat down, relieved. Ever since he had been birched

he had been more or less ostracised in the street. The riots, and the still missing loot from it was a sore point with the Jacks. They had long memories and nobody wanted their roving eyes floating over the district. For the moment, until things died down, Sniff was taboo. Perhaps we could try to help him again, beside, I was curious to hear what the Birch was all about. I had never met anyone who had had it.

"Tell us what 'appened," I invited as he sat down.

"Yeah, come on Sniff," urged Fatty, eager for the gory details, "Did it 'urt?"

"Too bloody right it 'urt."

"Go on, tell us what 'appened," I insisted. He hesitated at the painful memory.

"Well, the old judge gave me a right rollickin' I cin tell y'. Then the old sod gave me the fish eye like, y'know? . . . three strokes 'e said, an' may this be a lesson to y' young man. I wondered what the 'ell 'e was on about until the old Scuffer standin' be'ind me tapped me on the shoulder an' said, 'Foller me'. Next thing I knew I was next door with me trousers down, leanin' over a table with me arms out."

"Was there anyone else there?" asked Henry.

"Oh aye, three of'm altogether, the Scuffer an' two others dressed like toffs. There was me in me bare arse, wonderin' what the 'ell was gonna 'appen then, *wallop* . . . Jesus . . . Oh sorry 'enry, I forgot, you're gonna be a priest aren't y'?"

Henry nodded solemnly as Sniffer shook his head at the memory. "By Christ it didn't 'alf sting I'll tell y'."

"What did y' do then?" asked Fatty, agog with interest. I looked at him disgustedly.

"Don't be so flamin' daft Fatty. What d'y' think 'e did, 'ollered like a stuck pig, I'll bet." Sniffer shook his head.

"No, I didn't."

"Cor 'ell," exclaimed Fatty, "I woulda done."

"So would I," snapped Sniffer, "But I didn't 'ave bloody time did I?, 'e walloped me twice more. I 'ad a numb bum for an hour, then it 'urt."

"What did they do then?" asked Tommy.

"Nothin'. One of the toffs came over an' took a gander at me whatsit an' said it was O.K. I wish 'ed flamin' well asked me. The Scuffer told me t' get me kecks back on, an' that was that."

"Was that all?" ejaculated Fatty.

"What d'y' mean all?" demanded Sniffer. "Wasn't that enough? . . . an' then when I got 'ome, me Dad battered me."

"What for?" I asked, "Gerrin the birch?" Sniffer snorted disgustedly.

"Not 'im. You know me ole man, 'e wouldn't give a bugger if they birched me all day. 'e battered me for gerrin' caught."

There was a burst of spontaneous laughter. That figured. Mr Johnson just about had enough sense to come in out of the rain.

"Was it a cane?" asked Henry.

"Na, a bunch'a twigs or sommat, y'know, like wanna them broom things only smaller. Anyroad, warrever it was I don't wanna see it again. As far as I'm concerned they cin stuff it from now on."

"Warrabout the others?" asked Dinny.

"Oh they're still inside. I 'eard on the grapevine they're for the Cat. An' bloody good luck to 'em I say. They tell me that's real leather with nine tails on it, and they strap you up for it. I'll tell y' one thing though."

"Yeah?" queried Dinny.

"I'll lay ten t' one they won't roll anymore drunks after they've 'ad a basin fulla that."

I shuddered inwardly. One of Dad's mates had had the Cat before I was born. I had heard it mentioned several times as I grew up. Whatever they did to him he was apparently, a changed man afterwards. Saved jail space too, was Uncle Mat's opinion. He was a great one for the swift punishment was Uncle Mat, especially for thugs. If he had his way he would give them a taste of their own medicine and knock hell out of them. Given a chance on the Bench I think he would have put Judge Jeffries in the shade, in the hanging line at least. As he always said, it might not cure crime, but by hell it wouldn't 'alf thin 'em out. Sure as 'ell they wouldn't come back twice.

"Well," broke in Henry emphatically, "It's their own fault."

"Aw come off it, 'enry" said Sniffer, "We've all nicked stuff an' you know it."

"There's nickin' an' nickin'," replied Henry solemnly, "Sure we've nicked fruit an' free rides on the Ferry an' stuff like that, but we didn't 'urt no one, did we? It's not like clobberin' someone an' nickin' their wages is it? That's real nickin' that is."

" 'enry's right," said Tom, straightening his cramped legs. "There's one thing nickin' a few apples, but batterin' a bloke an' nickin' 'is wages, well that's somethin' else. I say they deserve all they get, an' then some."

For half an hour or so it felt quite like old times as the argument warmed up and I felt a pang of regret that soon, too soon, the gang would split up for good. Within a couple of weeks Henry would be off to a proper school. I secretly envied him his chance He would learn things we had never even dreamed of, but I envied Tommy even more. Within days of Henry going, he too would be off to join the Army. I would dearly have liked to have gone with him, but mention the Army to Dad and it was like waving a red rag to a bull. It was Fatty as usual who brought the discussion to an end.

"Look," he said peevishly, "Warra we gonna do this afternoon? Time's wastin', warrabout the Market?" he suggested, naming one of our favourite Saturday afternoon venues. There was a chorus of approval, and within minutes, accompanied by a 'Reformed' Sniffer, we were on our way.

Looking back I suppose the old market was one of the greatest free shows in the country. The sharp witted crowds had everything laid on free. 'Cock-shys', 'Beat the Goalie', Escape artists, Magicians and Evangelists from almost every faith except Catholics and Church of England.

Among this galaxy of entertainment threaded a constant parade of high stepping Coolies from the many ships in dock, who, to our great delight, always walked in single file, lifting their knees as though they were walking through high grass.

We had had hours of fun as schoolboys, falling in behind them and mimicking their peculiar walk as they wandered, wide eyed and chattering incessantly, among the stalls. Dinny nudged me as a group entered the open market just ahead of us.

"Yeh remember the docks?" he asked as the jinking line passed us. I burst out laughing, although I hadn't laughed the day it happened three years before, because I ran full tilt into Dad during the escape and got the daylights whaled out of me. It had all happened quite innocently when Henry, angel faced as always, said he wanted to go to the lavatory as we walked over the bridges towards a small seaside town on the other side of the docks.

The only lavatories on the dockside in those days was a single trough affair with open fronted cubicles giving as little privacy as possible. The whole thing depended for cleanliness on the automatic flush near the entrance. This went every few minutes, sending a flood of water down the length of the trough. Henry's eyes shone with unholy glee as he came out.

"Y'know what?" he said mysteriously as he re-joined us.

"What?" I asked.

"We couldn't 'alf tickle that lot up in there," he said, nodding towards the lavatory.

"Whaddy y' mean?" asked Sniffer.

"There's a load of Coolies in there. All the cubicles is full."

"Got y'," exclaimed Dinny, seeing the possibilities in a flash, "Get some paper."

"What's goin' on?" I asked, never having seen this one before.

"You'll see," replied Dinny, "Jus' get some paper, quick."

96

There was plenty about and within minutes we had a loose bundle.

"Ask that feller for a match," commanded Dinny, with a nod towards a passing docker. Fatty was gone and back in seconds with the match.

"Right, we're in. Now listen." Howls of laughter arose as Dinny explained the plan.

"Cor, flippin' 'eck," yelled Sniffer, "That should make 'em go a bit."

It did. With the rest of the gang keeping 'Decks' for anyone being 'caught short' and who might spoil the fun by coming in, Dinny went just inside the door, timed the next flush and, a split second before it came, set alight to the paper and flung it in. The results were instantaneous. Pandemonium broke out as the six Coolies got the hot seat. We scattered like quail as they shot out, chattering like monkeys as they hauled at their trousers. My luck was right out. Head down, arms going like pistons, and screaming with delight, I cannoned into a group coming through the railway gates. I looked up. It was Dad. He took one look at the dancing Coolies, put two and two together and got four.

"I'll see you later," was all he said. He did. The Coolies weren't the only ones with scorched bottoms that night. I couldn't prove it, but I knew Mam had been laughing. I could tell. We all had a good laugh at the memory, as the line passed out of our sight among the stalls.

"I'll lay ten t' one y' didn't tell that t' the Bishop when y' went for y' interview Hen'," said Dinny. Henry laughed. Suddenly the conversation changed to an even more popular subject.

"Look at them there Judies," said Dinny with a knowledgeable air, "Cor!" He rubbed his hands in silent appreciation. I looked at him disgustedly. More and more these days he kept on about girls. What the hell he could see in them I couldn't fathom out.

"Aw, come on," I said peevishly, "Never mind them, lets 'ave a gander round. Anyroad," I added, playing a trump card, " 'enry can't go 'angin' round Judies, can y' 'en?"

Henry grinned but remained silent.

"What's up with Judies?" demanded Sniffer, not aware as an Orangeman, of the intricacies of the Catholic faith.

"Y' kiddin'," broke in Fatty scathingly, "Did y' ever see a priest with a Judy?, use y' noddle for Chri . . . Sorry Hen'."

"Look, Din," I coaxed, "Never mind them, let's go an' 'ave a look at the Cock Shy, we might gerra coconut."

"Stuff the coconuts, I'm gonna chat that big'un up over there." He nodded towards a well upholstered girl who used to be at school with us."

"Please y'self, I'm gonna 'ave a listen to O'Flynn."

"OK," he replied equitably, "If I don't click with 'er I'll see y' over by the Cock Shy. If I do click, I'll see y' after Mass termorrer."

We parted, Dinny with a mysterious gleam in his eye, and the rest of us towards the biggest con-man I have ever known, O'Flynn, the only bald headed man who had the neck to sell hair restorer. I reckon he could have sold sand to the Arabs if he put his mind to it. His rich Irish brogue poured over the crowd like syrup as we approached, and for a good half hour we laughed with the crowd as he paraded his latest 'Miracle' cures and explained for the millionth time that his own pate was as it was 'By the Grace of God' and the gift he had was for the benefit of others! Our attention was at last diverted by a roar of laughter from the crowd near the 'Beat the Goalie' pitch. We raced over and arrived in time to see an unnerving sight.

One of the many itinerate performers lay stripped to the waist on the bare cobbles, supporting across his chest a slab of concrete. Apparently he had challenged anyone from the crowd to use the sledge hammer provided, to break the concrete.

Half an hour either side of three o'clock he would have been home and dry, but it had just turned three and the pubs were throwing out. A group of sailors and dockers, half seas over, had joined the crowd and his challenge had been accepted by a glassy-eyed docker. The crowd fell silent as he stood, hammer in his hands, swaying slightly as he tried to line the concrete up. I held my breath as the performer, wild-eyed with fear, waited. If he refused the challenge he would be laughed out of business. If he went on with it he stood a fair chance of staying on the market for ever. Twice the docker picked the hammer up and twice his reflexes failed him.

"Go on," encouraged the crowd, "You cin do it. 'ave a bash."

"For Jesus sake," cried the sweating performer, "Someone else 'ave a go."

His lack of faith was plain for all to see as he crossed his legs hopefully.

"Yeh challenged 'im," yelled one of the dockers' mates, "So lay still. Are y' scared?" he added in the understatement of the year.

"God almighty," gasped Sniffer, subdued for once, " 'e'll splatter 'im all over the market." It was a distinct possibility. As the hammer raised for the third time I glanced at the man on the ground. Legs crossed, eyes tight closed, he gripped the concrete like a lifebelt. You could almost see his guardian angel wringing his hands. There was a blare of movement. The crowd gasped as the hammer hit the concrete with a shuddering thump, then a cheer arose as it split in two. The performer staggered to his feet amid a roar of approval.

"Good on y' mate," said the striker as pennies hit the ground in appreciation all round the shaken man, " 'ere, 'ave a swig at this," he pulled a small whisky bottle from his pocket and handed it over, but his generousity was short lived as the performer gulped at it desperately. The docker grabbed his bottle back with a snarl.

"I said a swig mate, not the 'ole bloody bottle."

I never saw him perform again. I reckon he must have taken up knitting or something, but one of the other performers, an escapologist we did see later in the week, performing outside the Yard. He too dropped a clanger.

Some Mateloes off a destroyer in dock, took up his challenge to tie him up. The poor bloke was still struggling to escape when the knocking off buzzer went.

It was a dangerous place for performers. There were too many comedians about. I suppose on reflection it was natural. You had to be a comedian to live there.

8

Farewell Fatty

1936 was a cataclysmic year for me. I had everything yet
suddenly I seemed to have nothing. At home, all was peace
and plenty . . . no, not plenty, but enough. I had two
pairs of boots, a miracle in itself. I had a regular job and
spends of a shilling a week, yet withal I felt destitute.
Within one traumatic month of our outing to the market,
the close comradeship of the gang was completely broken.
Henry had taken his first shaky steps on the road to priesthood, Tommy strutted the parade ground in the full
glory of the uniform he had always wanted and Sniffer,
of all the screaming idiots had, despite his fervent
promises to steer clear of the trouble makers, allowed
himself to be conned into another lookout for some new
mates, and was now getting a touch of the real thing in
Borstal. Actually, as it turned out later, it was the best
thing that ever happened to him, but he didn't think so
when they carted him off.

Bonko Armfield, dainty as an elephant as always,
slipped on a plank in the Yard when he went to look for a
job and broke his leg in two places. Dinny, already far gone
in the mysteries of courtship with our old school col-
league, seemed to be suffering from severe softening of
the brain and continually drooled. My only regular companion in the evenings was Fatty, and he was murder. He
followed me everywhere like a melancholy ghost. The
gang had taken a battering and I felt lost without them.

Henry I missed especially. I missed his calmness, his
dry sense of humour, but most of all I missed his steadying influence. If anyone talked reason in the gang it was

him, the rest of us just reacted. I leaned against the lampost at the bottom of the street in the late autumn sunshine and kicked a pebble disconsolately as I waited for Fatty to turn up and hoping against hope that Dinny would show up too.

What was Henry doing now I wondered, as the scene of his leaving danced in my mind's eye. An involuntary smile twitched my lips as I remembered his embarrassment as we shook hands in the final parting. Unaccustomed sentimentality had crept in as he had looked at me solemnly.

"I wish you were comin' Li," he said, holding his small suitcase and fidgetting uncomfortably in the first suit he had ever owned.

"Go on," I joshed him, "Cin y' see me bein' a priest? God'd 'ave a fit. You'll be alright Hen', probably finish up as Pope or sommat."

Mrs Fielding, proud as a peacock as she stood protectively behind him, had laughed. "I don't think 'e'll get that far Liam, but 'e'll do well, you'll see."

I looked at the thin emaciated face and the deep set eyes haunted by the constant worry of a sick husband and four younger children still to bring up on nothing. Like all our mothers she had looked forward almost desperately for Henry to leave school and get a job, but it was not to be. He was just meant for the priesthood and the lads knew it. Father Mac had seen it too and warned him a hundred times that the going would be rough, but in the end, with the aid of the Bishop's fund, made up from pennies, halfpennies and even farthings collected every Sunday throughout all parishes, he was on his way. For the family it was near disaster. He had to be kitted out and it took the combined efforts of aunts, uncles and neighbours to do it. Now he was gone and I worried in case he couldn't stand the harsh regime. Life would be spartan and discipline strict. Up at six thirty, adequate, and only adequate food, at least he was used to that. At fourteen and with his background he would have a hard slog to get his Higher School certificate because then and only then would he start to study for the priesthood. Another two years Philosophy, followed by another four in Theology. No contact with anyone on a normal day to day level such as we had known. No pubs, no shops or cafés, nothing, just discipline and healthy games and study. If he survived all this and reached the Philosophy stage he would have his head tonsured, at least this was no problem, we were all used to Mr Fenshaw's tuppenny all off's, then he could stagger through the seven orders of priesthood. Door-keeper, Reader, Exorcist, Acolyte, sub-Deacon, Deacon, and finally Priest. I didn't envy him, I don't think I could have made doorkeeper, never mind the rest. Still it was what he wanted and his whole family had the pawn tickets to prove it. He seemed smaller as I took his delicate hand for the last time. I felt awkward.

"See y' at Christmas Hen'."

"If God spares y'," added Fatty in the time honoured phrase.

Dinny, standing alongside us had laughed as he added the rest of the saying.

"Ah, God's good, an' the Divil's not bad to his own."

"We'll 'ave t' go now Henry love," broke in Mrs Fielding gently, "They'll all be waitin' at the station."

Henry's new boots squeaked expensively as he turned, a sure sign that they were new.

"Can't we wait a minute Mam? I won't see them for a long time."

She shook her head anxiously.

"You've a long journey ahead of y' lad. Anyroad, y' Aunties'll be waitin'. Come on love, say tarrar."

I felt strangely dumb as he turned again, eyes misted. I tried a joke but nothing came. Dinny, practical as always, came to my aid.

"Come on Hen' you'll 'ave the flippin' Pope after y'. You'd berra git."

"If y' see Tommy on 'is next leave, tell 'im I was askin' after 'im will y'? Oh an' don't forget Sniffer." We nod-ded silently. He smiled wanly then lowered his head in

103

embarrassment as he noticed every neighbour in the street watching him go. I can still see him, his Mam's arm round his shoulder as they passed the neighbours. Even the Orange families wished him luck. They turned at the corner, past the lampost under which we had spent so many happy hours together, then, with a final wave he was gone.

"What the 'ell's up with you?" Dinny's harsh but welcome voice roused me from my reverie. He looked at me anxiously.

"What's up with y'?" he repeated, "I spoke to y' twice, thought you'd snuffed it or sommat. Are y' alright?" I grinned.

"Just thinkin' about 'enry, y'know, dreamin' like. Anyroad, never mind that, are y' comin' out t'night?"

"Nope, just come t' tell y' summat . . . We're movin'."

"Y'what?"

"Movin'. Me Mam's gorra Corporation 'ouse."

"Y' kiddin'."

"No, straight up. Wanna them posh one's up the North End."

I looked at him flabbergasted. That's all I needed. It was bad enough him chasing girls but to move from the street. Hells Bells."

"It's gorra garden too," he announced proudly.

"Oh," I said, "Touch me not, me Dad's a bobby."

"Wot y' bein' sarky for?" he demanded, "Its gonna be berra than this dump." He nodded towards the tight packed street that had been our world for so long.

"When're y' goin'?" I asked despondently.

"When me Mam shifts 'erself I suppose." Suddenly I felt mad.

"What the 'ell's everybody movin' for?" I demanded, "What's going on?"

"Whaddy y' mean?" he asked, perplexed. "If you've gorra move, you've gorra move, 'aven't yeh? Blimey, you're in a right bloody mood aren't y'?"

"Well," I said defensively.

104

"Anyroad I just come t' ask will y' give us a 'and t' move?"

"Can't y' come out with me an' Fatty?"

"I've gorra date. Anyroad, what's the use with all the lads away? Besides I'm courtin'."

I gazed at his shining face and slicked down hair. Even with a tide mark round his neck I had to admit he looked a lot better than he used to. He even had an old collar on instead of the usual muffler. He still looked scruffy but in a more sedate sort of way.

"What're y' all tarted up for?" I demanded. His eyes caught sight of his new love, Annie Cochrane, coming down the street. He beamed.

"Hech, hech," he said urgently, "Annie's comin'."

I looked disgustedly at the fiery-haired, buxom, sixteen year old easing her bulk towards us. She looked what she was, an obliging sort of girl. He nudged me confidentially.

"What d'y' reckon?" he asked.

"I wouldn't touch it with a fifty foot barge pole mate," I snapped, "Look at it."

"I am," he said, rubbing his hands gleefully.

Annie, like a tug in turbulent water, tacked to port to avoid a puddle, then berthed smoothly alongside us. Dinny looked at her with quiet lechery, doubtless admiring her matching tide-mark and black finger nails as she coyly replaced a straying hair. Her greeting was in keeping with her appearance.

"Hi ya Din," she said airily, " 'ow's y' belly for spots?"

"Not bad, an' gerrin' betta," he replied, slipping his arm through hers and giving her an exploratory squeeze. She giggled.

"Hey, knock it off Din," she cried archly, wriggling in her oversize dress as his explorations went astray. He released his arm and straightened his battered tie with unconscious grandeur. I felt sickened. A good mate, a brother almost literally drooling. If that's what girls did to a fella they could stick them, I thought savagely.

"See y' in church," he said airily, then, followed by my heavy scowl they strolled like a couple of off-beat toffs up the street. They had scarcely covered fifty yards when Fatty came skidding round the corner and straight into my pent up emotions.

"Where the bloody 'ell 'ave you bin?" I snapped. He gazed at me wide eyed, "Anyroad," I continued before he could speak, "I'm goin' 'ome, I'm fed up."

"Suits me," he said without any sign of rancour. I looked at him astonished.

"Whaddy y' mean?" I snapped.

"I've clicked" he said jubilantly. My heart sank. Not him too?

"You've what?" I cried.

"I told y'," he answered cockily, "I've clicked. Cor . . . y' wanna see 'er." He indicated a shapely form with his hands. "Anyroad y' know her, she used t' be in our class, y'know, May Williams. I gazed at his round palpitating form in horror.

"Y' want y' bloody bumps read mate," I said disgustedly. He bridled at the implied insult to his taste.

"Whaddy y' mean?" he demanded indignantly.

"She's flamin' cross-eyed." I snapped unfeelingly.

"So what?"

"She's as daft as a bloody brush, so's 'er ole woman."

"So what?" he asked again. "Cross-eyed or not mate, she knows what it's all about, that's good enough for me."

"Wharrabout me?" I demanded. He looked at me amazed.

"Wharrabout you?" he asked, spitting on his hand and slicking his hair down.

"Well" I said defensively, "Dinny's gone off with Annie, you're off with whatsit, warram I gonna do by meself?"

"Get y'self a Judy," he answered with a grin, "It's great."

I felt betrayed. Girls had never entered my head. The thought of actually being alone with one terrified me. I was suddenly alone, the gang had gone and my world had turned upside down. I looked at the excited face in front of me.

"Oh bugger off," I said in despair, "I'll see y' termorrer at work."

If I could have foreseen what the next forty-eight hours would bring I would have tied him to the lamppost rather than see him go. It was one of the worst evenings I spent throughout the whole of my younger life. Even the pork pie that Mam had saved specially for my supper failed to lighten the terrible feeling of depression that settled over me.

There are days in one's life which stand out with startling clarity however long one lives. The last Monday in August 1936 was such a day. Dinny, myself and Fatty, our newest recruit to the shipyard, allowed Dad and Con to draw ahead of us as I was regaled with the gory details of their two dates the previous night. Dinny, the most experienced in this new venture, was ecstatic in his descriptions of the delights of female company, whilst Fatty, despite the leg pulling over his cross-eyed love, stoutly upheld his end. Mad though I was at their desertion, I could not help but be enthralled by the exultant details of their innocuous stroll through the park. The heady entertainment of two ice creams and a Sassparilla apiece in a local hostelry, and the final gruesome details of undercover territorial explorations of the female form.

For Dinny, the evening ended on an exultant note, the details of which I will not describe. For poor Fatty it ended with his love getting a belt over the ear from her irate father. What Fatty was going to do to him when he grew up was nobody's business. There was no question that he, unlike Dinny, who was a born opportunist, was in love, and he was still talking of her as we walked through the time office and down into the Plater's shed. We were just about to leave for our respective work places when Con called me back.

"Hey," he said, glaring at me, "What's all this I've jus' bin' 'earin'?"

"All what?" I queried.

"Don't come the innocent with me," he snapped, "You know warr'I'm talkin' about. All this arsin' around in the dinner break, that's what." I laughed at his concern.

"We're only 'avin' a birra fun," I said lightly. Dad, hearing Con's voice raised, left his mates and came across.

"What's up?" he asked bluntly.

"Jus' warnin' 'im about larkin' around aboard ship durin' dinner time. Y'know what they're like." Dad nodded.

"Knock it off," he said warningly, "You'll break y' bloody neck racin' round on board. Any bloody nonsense an' you'll 'ave y' dinner 'ere with us . . . gorrit?"

I nodded respectfully. For weeks now, with our new friends in the Yard, we had bolted our sandwiches down then spent the rest of the dinner hour playing about the maze of girders and planks of the half finished ship. It was a perfect playground, and with the whole of the ship to ourselves until the one o'clock buzzer went, we made the most of it, especially since this new craze for girls had made any sort of street games impossible after work. With the instinctive stupidity of youth, all the games we had played in the streets, Tick Illyallyo, and a dozen other racing games, now became even more exciting sixty or seventy feet up on the skeleton ship where just one slip would be enough. Dinny sprang to my aid.

"Don't worry Mr Sullivan, we're not daft. We don't take no chances . . . Honest."

"Just watch it," replied Dad seriously, "Y' don't bounce when y' 'it the deck y'know. Just use y' noddles and keep outa trouble. Go on, buzz off."

We turned gratefully and raced towards the ship to get our fires going and the rivets ready for the first call, but we had no intention of cutting out the games.

At twelve o'clock the buzzer went. At five past, Fatty joined us from the Engine shop where he drilled holes in small turbine rotor blades, and by twelve thirty, our sandwiches safely inside us, we joined the crowd of Hotting Lads swarming like monkeys about sixty feet up. The game, Illyallyo, had actually started the previous Friday and with two teams playing, it was our turn to be 'In'.

A very popular game in the streets, it required one team to chase the other over a strictly defined area. The chasers also provided a prison in which the captured members of the other team were kept. These prisoners could be released by the simple expedient of dashing through the prison like a maniac shouting 'Illyallyo' as one went through, where upon all the prisoners were allowed to go free and the game continued with the object of capturing all the opposing team and keeping them shut up. On the streets the game could and did go on for days, taking it up where it left off the previous day. On board ship with only planks, girders and half built decks to run along it became positively hair-raising.

We had been going less than ten minutes in the blazing sunshine when, with dramatic suddenness fun turned to stark tragedy. With the 'prison' situated in the half completed 'Tween Decks', one deck down from the main deck, Fatty, one of the few still free, had the brilliant notion of taking a short cut across a 'tween deck girder which was partly obscured from the guards' view, and releasing the prisoners.

Unused to shipboard life and certainly not built for speed, he got halfway across, then with open space all round him, froze. Dinny spotted him first.

"Jesus!" he exclaimed, clasping his hand to his mouth in horror, "The stupid sod's stopped. Look." I looked across and went cold inside. Fatty, less than fifteen feet away, face chalk white, stood frozen on the narrow girder. In a flash the game was forgotten. All hands rushed to the end of the girder. Advice flooded the air.

"For Christ's sake shurrup will y'?" I yelled, panic stricken in case he fell into the abyss of criss crossed girders and planks below him. The crowd went silent.

"Fatty," called Dinny in a strangled half whisper, "Don't look down, keep lookin' at us. You'll be alright. We'll gerra rope across to y'." I looked at him incredulously. There was no way that we could get a rope to him. Even if we could, what the hell could he do with it?"

"Fetch the Blocker Man," I snapped to the nearest lad to me, " 'ell know what t' do."

By this time the 'tween deck around us was crowded with drawn anxious faces. They all knew the score. A deathly, incredible silence descended. I was about to speak again.

"Leave it," hissed a heavy voice in my ear as we were pushed unceremoniously along what firm space there was, "Just leave it, I'll try an' talk 'im across."

In an atmosphere that could be cut, the stranger, like a mother crooning to her child, began to talk softly, caressingly against a background that threatened to explode any moment as the Yard started up again.

"Y' alright lad. Now jus' take it easy there. Do as I tell y' now."

Fatty, every fibre in his corpulent body rigid, stood like a glassy-eyed statue. I felt myself sweating. Dinny, alongside me gripped my arm until it hurt.

"Cin y' 'ear me?" said the stranger softly. Fatty moved his head imperceptibly.

"Now listen careful lad. Jus' ease y'self down, gently. Bend y' knees slowly, very slowly." Fatty, eyes bulging and fixed on some point far below him, did not move a muscle.

"Are y' listenin'?" Again Fatty's head moved a fraction as the gathering crowd waited in tense silence.

"Come on now," encouraged the stranger, "Jus' do as I tell y', you'll be alright.

Slowly now, bend y' knees an' take a hold of the girder with y' 'ands."

A sibilant hiss arose as his knees began to bend. Every nerve in me screamed with terror as he suddenly wavered, then steadied. Suddenly, with an ear splitting scream that made everybody jump, the one o'clock buzzer hit the air like a Banshee. A petrified ripple ran round the deck as Fatty froze solid again. The grimy stranger, eyes staring, face grey with strain tried desperately to soothe him.

"Y' alright now. It was only the buzzer. Y' doin' well, y'nearly there, jus' bend y' knees a bit more an' take a hold."

Again the crowd held its breath as his knees began to bend against a cacophony of noise as the Yard got into its stride again. I looked at Dinny. He was chalk white. My left arm ached from the pressure of his fingers gripping me.

Mother of God, I thought, he couldn't fall. He mustn't fall.

Inch by inch his hands came to the girder, then a sigh of relief swept us all as they touched, then grasped it.

"Great," encouraged the stranger, wiping beads of sweat from his forehead, "Just 'old on now and listen. You've gorra sit down. Gently now, take y' left foot off an' squat down a bit."

Slowly Fatty's backside edged towards the girder.

"Good on y' lad. Now, lean forward an' take the weight on y' 'ands a bit."

His shoulders went forward obediently.

"Now put y' left knee against the girder t' steady y'self a bit, gently now."

Nicely balanced, and with his seat comfortably on his right heel, all that remained was to ease his backside on to the girder and he would be more than half way home. Then, for some unaccountable reason he suddenly froze solid again.

All the honeyed words in the world could not save him as he began to sway gently. Sudden, terrifying fear gripped me. Dinny and I exchanged horrified glances as the sway deepened, then the hair on the back of my neck rose as an animal scream tore at the air as he fell. For what seemed an age the helpless doll-like figure bounced sickeningly among the maze of girders until he lay, far, far below in a bloodied crumpled heap on the bilge plates. I stared at it disbelievingly. It couldn't be true. Poor Fatty, just fifteen and in the throes of his first love! In his short bitter life he had had nothing, seen nothing and done nothing. Oh God, what is it all about, and where the hell are y'?"

9

Paid Holiday

I suppose it is one of life's ironies that one can live with a person, or in a place, all one's life and never know either. It was even more ironic that it was as a result of Fatty's horrifying death that I finally came to know Dad.

Mam of course I knew like a well-loved book. Her every expression had its meaning for me as though written in foot high letters. Harsh, practical, fiercely loyal and a strict disciplinarian, I knew all her moods, but Dad, well, he was just Dad. He came and went, sometimes easygoing, sometimes irritable, always swift in his discipline, yet, in his own inimitable way, scrupulously fair with all of us. He had, over the years, treated me with what I can only describe as distant affection. Only on one occasion, when I was about eight, and ill for the first time, did he really show his inner self. For the four days I was ill he almost smothered me with affection. With Fatty's death all that changed, quietly but definitely.

From that moment I had to report to him in the Plater's shop within minutes of the dinner buzzer going. For the first few days I resented this pennance bitterly, then, on the day after the funeral just as Dinny, who had loyally shared this supervision, and I were opening our dinner tins, Dad turned to me.

"Get them there down quick," he said, "I wanna show y' somethin'."

"What?"

"Just eat y' dinner, you'll see. I'm gonna show y' around the Yard, well, a bit of it anyroad. If y' gonna work 'ere it's about time y' knew what it's all about, for y' own good."

"Cin I come?" Dad looked across at Dinny and grinned. "Yeah, why not. You've gorra lot t' learn too."

It may seem strange to the reader that we should have been reared within sight and sound of the place and now worked in it, yet did not really know a thing about it, much less have seen it all, but this was true of many of the workers.

It was so huge, so varied that men kept strictly to their own particular sections, but Dad was not one of them. He knew every nook and cranny in the place, and stored away in his mind a wealth of detail that took me by surprise. For the six weeks that I remained there, between the accident and when I left it for good, he poured out this knowledge in a series of dinner hour lessons that I remember even today. It was fascinating. Our regular tours began with a visit to the Dry Dock to watch a merchant ship edge its way through the gates from the Mersey behind her. He laughed as I plied him with a thousand questions. With a patience I never knew he possessed, he explained just how it was done. How the ship was centred on the huge plumb line that dropped down at the bow end of the dock. The close cooperation between the signalling Blockerman standing quayside above the plumb line, and the ship's officers in the cabin. We watched breathlessly as the giant timber baulks were dropped neatly between the ship's sides and the dock to hold her steady after she was lined correctly and before she was dropped on to the waiting stocks below her submerged keel as the water was pumped out. It was one of the shortest dinner hours I ever spent, and both Dinny and I felt cheated as the buzzer screeched over our heads to call us back to the grind. I was at the Plater's shed in record time for the next promised tour of the dock itself, a tour which proved even more breath-taking than the docking itself, as we went down the steep steps and stood under the ship.

It was an odd, frightening experience to stand in this vast, tomb-like structure with an ocean going vessel balanced on the stubby wooden blocks less than four feet above us. Dad explained, in a crouched-back tour under the vessel, the reason for its docking, a twisted propellor blade which, within hours had been removed and was even now in the repair shop. But it was the barnacles clinging to the bottom that fascinated me most. Thousands of them clustered tightly to the metal plates and already being removed by scores of workmen as they raced against time to clean and paint her bottom before the propellor was repaired and fitted for her departure within the week.

He showed us the deep drainage channels down either side of the dock and where to look for crabs in them. We examined the giant stone chutes running from dockside to dock floor down which heavy equipment could be shot when required. He laughed uproariously at my sudden panic as I realised that all that stood between us and the murky river outside were the massive steel gates through which the ship had come. I believed him when he said they wouldn't burst, but I still kept half an eye on them. Day after day our food was bolted and we were on our way. The Engine shop, where the giant turbines were made and moved about by enormous overhead cranes running on gantries high overhead on either side of the shop. The Pattern shop, where they made 'Templates' for marking out plates and a hundred other things. The Welders, Painters, Scalers, chipping away the rust from inside boilers. It seemed endless. Then, for three glorious dinner hours he guided us round the fascinating fitting out of a refrigeration ship in the Wet dock, or 'Basin' as they called it. We gazed in wonder at the miles of electric cables, the huge refrigeration holds packed with endless tubes from which hung hooks to hold the carcases. It was another world, a world I had never dreamed of, where men swarmed like ants to work a miracle of construction. For three whole weeks, without a hint of complaint, he gave us the full benefit of his knowledge of the Yard, then out of the blue, he gave us the biggest surprise to date. Somehow he had wangled permission for us to see the Mammoth, the enormous floating crane moored in the Basin, said to be the biggest in the world at that time. Not only did we see it, we actually went aboard, climbed the dizzy height and gazed open mouthed at the view through the cabin window. For the first time I actually saw the Mersey and the torrid activity on it. Ferry boats, criss crossing in endless succession. Dredgers, chugging the twenty-one miles up river to dump their loads at the 'Bar' forming the river mouth, Freighters, Oil tankers, arrogant Pilot boats and a myriad other craft waltzing and skittering in ordered chaos on the turgid, heaving water, and above them all, in constant vigil, the Liver Birds on top of the Liver buildings on the Liverpool side. But an even greater privilege was to come, an experience given to few outside a shipyard, and, strangely enough, one not seen by all who work there, a full launch.

For two days before the scheduled launch we watched the frantic preparations round the newly built ship, the heavy greasing of the slipway down which it would plunge, the fixing of the massive drag chains down either side of the ship to hold its enormous weight in check as it gathered speed. Then, on the great day itself we joined the packed, expectant crowd waiting for the high point of the tide.

Arm around my shoulders, he explained in graphic detail all that would happen once the bottle smashed against its side.

Bang on time I watched in breathless excitement as a lady, obviously a toff stood on the platform built snugly high up on the bow, bottle raised in her hand. Smash, it shattered into a thousand pieces. With split-second timing the man in charge of the slipway gang gave the signal to slip the holding gear. She shuddered and began to move, then, with hellish noise that scared the living daylights out of me, she began to gather way. With drag chains writhing and screeching like tormented monsters she tore at the restraining bonds. Amid a cloud of blue smoke as the grease burnt under the crushing weight she stormed her way majestically to the river. Seconds later, amid a tumultuous roar from the crowd and the shrieking sirens of her sisters already water-born, she hit the brown water in a welter of spray. For one terrifying moment I thought she was going under, then, as the bow end struck, her stern lifted and she floated clear, amid the debris of her birth. Within seconds the ruthless river had her in its grip, the stern began to swing under the force of the current, but the two tiny tugs, stationed at exactly the right distance, darted in like terriers. There was a blur of frantic activity as they closed in and with the expertise of a lifetime the tiny figures on board both tugs and ship, quickly secured the towing ropes and her brief period of freedom was ended. It was a tremendous thrill, but looking back I think the thing that made it so was Dad, standing with me. Never before had we been so close.

Thoughts of the launch still filled my mind as the five o'clock buzzer went and the second and most important event of the day caught me completely unawares. I was still riddling my fire and preparing it with fresh coke for an early start next morning when Dad's voice sounded below. I looked down to see him and Con waving frantically for me to come down.

"What's up?" I asked anxiously as I hit the bottom rung. Con grinned broadly.

"Nuthin's up, I think I've gorra job for y'. A good job." I gaped at him.

"Where at?"

"The Railway," broke in Dad, "On the vans. Holy Sailor Li, if y' get that you'll be quids in."

He wasn't kidding either. A job on the railways was a near impossibility. Like the Docks, it was a family job. Even though the wages were low, very low, outsiders rarely got a smell at it, as sons followed fathers. Its main attraction was that it was a constant job and therefore worth a king's ransom in this time of endemic unemployment. I couldn't believe it. Dad struck a note of caution.

"Well y' 'aven't gorrit yet. One'f Cons mates, y'know, Gerry Dolan, 'as purra word in for y', that's all."

"No one knows anythin' about it yet," added Con, "So

116

if y' look slippy an' keep y' nose clean, it's a good chance. Warrever y' do keep y' mouth shut 'til you've seen the Station Master . . . gorrit?" I nodded, he didn't need to remind me of that.

"When do I see 'im?" I asked anxiously.

"Termorrer, Gerry's already told 'im he knows a likely lad an' 'ell take y' down in the mornin'."

At eight o'clock sharp, with Gerry standing beside me, I was in the Station Master's office. I would lose half a day's pay and felt terrified as I looked up at the tall uniformed figure, but it was worth it. Gerry did most of the talking and the old boy seemed to take a fancy to me. At eight thirty I walked out of the office on air. Subject to a medical examination and a simple written test which was mandatory, the job was mine. Imagine, me a van boy on the Railway at seven and a tanner a week and uniform. Hell's Bells! What a stroke of luck! It would mean another day lost on Monday but with this shining prospect who cared?

Strangely I was more excited by my first train ride and journey away from home on my own than worried about the test at Chester station, fifteen miles up the line. The test seemed to go well, but the week that followed was one of the longest in my life. We were all on edge as the postman went by day after day, then with the four o'clock post on the Friday, it came. I'd got it!

Dad read and re-read the letter as he walked through the door after work. Mam was beside herself with excitement. At sixteen and a bit I had a constant job, the first in the family to do so.

"Thank God for that," said Dad as he finally handed me the magic letter, "You're outa the Yard, an' if y' keep y' nose clean y' could be there for life. Y' dead jammy."

He was right I was dead lucky and I knew it. I just couldn't wait to see Dinny to tell him. But now that he was living at the North End and in constant search for 'Crumpet' as he called it, that would have to wait until morning. With no gang to tell I bolted my tea and made the rounds of as many relatives as I could button hole and spent the whole evening basking in their collective praise.

Long before the official starting time next day I was outside the time office waiting for Dinny. At last, bleary-eyed and dishevelled, his left eye bruised, he came staggering through the gate.

"Cor strike a light Din, y' look as if you've bin dragged through an 'edge backwards. What y' bin doin'?" He rubbed his hand across his face wearily and winced.

"What 'appened?" I asked again, all thoughts of my new job vanishing in my concern.

"What 'appened?" he said savagely, "I'll tell y' what 'appened, I got flamin' well clobbered that's what, an' all because of this flamin' Judy."

"Oh?" I said, non-committally.

"Yeah," he continued as we walked to the ship, "Picked 'er up in the park, a right little cracker I'll tell y'. I thought, right mate, you're on 'ere. Just give 'er the chat an' y' well away."

"What 'app . . .?"

"I'm tellin' y'," he snapped, "I chatted 'er inter goin' for a gander round the docks," he winked painfully. "There's some great little places t' take a Judy round the docks" he added, giving me the benefit of his wide experience, "I'll show y' sometime."

I shrugged silently. "Anyroad," he continued, "There we were, gassin' fifty t' the dozen when we bump inter this feller near the dock gates. She took one look an' run like 'ell."

"What for?"

"It was 'er flamin' brother, that's what for. Honest, 'e looked more like a bloody gorilla than a bloke. Y' shoulda seen 'im."

"But you hadn't done anythin' 'ad y'?"

"Y' kiddin', what could I do with a Judy on the Dock Road in broad daylight? Anyroad 'e said, " 'oo are you?" An' before I could answer, the sod landed me one."

"What did y' do?"

118

"Y' jokin'," he said disgustedly, "Whaddy y' think I did? I ran like the clappers."

"Are y' gonna see 'er again?" He looked at me sombrely out of his good eye.

"Look mate, if I wanna commit suicide I'll jump in the flippin' dock." I laughed.

"That's what y' get muckin' about with Judies," I opined. He grinned.

"Yeah, I suppose y' right, y' can't win 'em all." He gave me a grotesque wink. "Never mind, I get me share," he added mysteriously. I couldn't wait any longer, I had to get my news out.

"Hey, I've got another job," I burst out. He looked at me incredulously.

"Y'what?"

"I told y', I've got another job . . . On the Railways . . . I start on the vans down the Ferry next Monday." He stopped and gazed at me.

"Of all the jammy sods! Honest Li if y' fell down the lavatory you'd come up with a gold watch."

Actually it was more than a gold watch I had come up with. From the moment I walked into the station on the following Monday I felt at home.

Gerry led me through the bustling scene in the main station to the Parcels Hall at the back. "There's your mate," he said, pointing to a stocky, rounded shouldered man of about forty, busily rummaging through a pile of parcels at the far end.

"Hey Jack," he called. My new mate, a bleary-eyed Welshman with a hand rolled cigarette dangling from the corner of his mouth, looked up, then in response to Gerry's wave, coughed his way towards us with a shuffling gait.

"This is Liam," announced Gerry cheerfully as Jack stopped in front of us and gazed at me suspiciously, "Y' new lad."

Jack surveyed me silently between coughs. I didn't like the look of his flickering bloodshot eyes. After a second or two he rumbled something unintelligible. I looked at Gerry uncertainly. He laughed.

"Ah take no notice of 'im Li, 'e always mutters in Welsh . . . don't y' Jack?"

Jack's watery eyes opened momentarily then closed again as smoke billowed into them, then his left eye opened and peered at me closely whilst he rolled the cigarette expertly from one side of his mouth to the other with his tongue.

" 'es no giant, is 'e boyo?" he said, giving my bicep an exploratory squeeze.

Gerry laughed. "Don't worry Jack 'es all there. Anyroad," he added, "I'm gonna load up, 'es all yours." He turned and gave me a wink as he saw the concern on my face, "Don't worry Li, 'e won't bite y', 'es always like this in the mornin' . . . arn't y' Jack? 'e can't 'elp it."

Jack gave him a piratical grin as the smoke got in his eyes again, then he stuck a piece of paper in my hand as Gerry left.

"Y' see them parcels by 'ere boyo?" he asked in a lilting voice and pointing with a mutilated index finger at the parcels he had been working at. I nodded.

"Sort 'em out." I looked at him blankly. He sniffed heavily and took another drag bringing on a new spasm.

"The list boyo, the list," he gasped, stabbing at the paper in my hand. I got the drift and, eager to start, turned. He grabbed my collar. The cigarette bounced up and down in his mouth as he gazed at me earnestly.

"Mark you boyo, I want it done right mind. No nonsense now, street order an' number order so they trot out smooth, y' understand?"

I didn't know what the devil he was talking about but I nodded intelligently. He seemed satisfied.

"Right," he said, taking another drag at the fast diminishing cigarette, "I'm off t' see Dolly now. She likes 'er sugar early."

Just my flaming luck I thought as I made my way to the parcels, a barmy Welshman! Everyone else in the hall seemed normal, why the hell did I have to drop for him.

120

He didn't even speak English properly. To my surprise neither did many of the others I passed. I got the feeling that only Gerry and I were English. It was all 'Boyo's here, and 'By 'ere's' there, I might just as well have been in Wales. Still it was the L.M.S. & G. Western.

For a while I immersed myself in the task in hand. Suddenly I became aware of a silent group of men watching me. I straightened in curiosity. A split second later I was grabbed, a hand clamped over my mouth and I was carried struggling like mad to the far side of the hall amid howls of laughter and dumped in an old tea chest. I didn't know what was happening. A knock on the side of the chest, followed by Gerry's voice as he sat on top of it, warned me to keep quiet. I caught on and played along. For a few seconds there was silence then Jack's slurring voice came through to me.

"There now," he yelled irately, "Would you believe it bach, 'es gone. Y' give 'em a job an' what 'appens eh? . . . Typical, bloody typical."

Expressions of surprise came from around the box. Nobody knew where I was. For five full minutes they let poor Jack ramp and rage about the younger generation before they let me out amid gales of laughter. By the way he joined in the fun it was obvious that he was used to having his leg pulled. I felt happy as I climbed out of the box. They were a good bunch and became even better as I got to know them.

Within half an hour, with the parcels sorted out to his satisfaction, he introduced me to 'Dolly'. We hit it off from the moment I scratched her velvet-like nose, and for the next six months we would be almost inseparable.

Although I had seen hundreds of horses round the streets and docks I had never really been in close proximity to them, except for the occasional pat given to those I knew well, like the milkman's or coalman's horses. To tell the truth, they scared me a little. But not Dolly, she was gorgeous, and at times almost human. Within days of our meeting Jack allowed me the rare privilege of curry-combing her, even though I had to stand on a box to do it. She loved it. He showed me how to plait her mane, then I added a bit of colour with a piece of blue ribbon. I will swear that she knew when I had polished her brasses and collar, for her head would be high as she leaned into the traces. But if I loved her, Jack, after a partnership of over five years positively doted on her. He was a most amazing man, rough, barely understandable when he spoke, or rather mumbled, he gave the impression of being an irritable old sod but he had a heart of pure gold. He was a good mate and as straight as a gun barrel. Now I had two Dads, I was indeed a fortunate boy.

Within a fortnight of starting the job, Dolly was due up for shoeing and I entered the mysterious world of the blacksmith's shop for the first time. Between them Jack and the blacksmith patiently answered a million questions as I watched the remains of the old shoes hacked off, her hooves dug out, pared and trimmed. I watched fascinated as the new shoes were made and fitted then, red hot, slammed on to the hoof. I actually winced as the nails were driven through, then out of the front of the hoof, where the ends were expertly nipped off and trimmed.

"Did it 'urt 'er?" Of course not, what the 'ell d'y' think I am, a butcher?

"Warrabout all the smoke when y' put the shoe on, that must 'ave 'urt 'er?"

"It always does that, if it 'ad 'urt 'er she'd 'ave jumped wouldn't she?" I was still dubious, so he showed me where the hoof was alive and where it was dead.

"What would 'appen if she didn't 'ave shoes on?" . . . "Would it hurt if she lost one?"

Why this, why that? The questions flooded out.

"God," said the blacksmith at one stage, "Is 'e like this all day Jack?" Jack grinned. "No, just most of it."

Still gasping in his eternal struggle with his cigarette he turned to me as the last shoe was being fitted.

"Come by 'ere bach an' shurrup or I'll gerr'im t' stick a pair on you."

Dolly seemed delighted with her new shoes as she pranced on the hard cobbles outside, liquid brown eyes wide, nostrils flaring as she whinnied with pleasure, but there was work to be done. She was quickly harnessed to the loaded van and we were off again. Our beat was the main shopping centre, and she knew every shop in it. Within a week she also got to know our house which lay on the way back to the station. She also got to know the sugar butty that Mam always gave her, whilst Jack and I had a cup of tea. It was a dreamlike existence after the jobs I had had. Free, happy, with a host of friends among my workmates and the shop-keepers we served, the time just flew by. It seemed incredible that I should have been selected for such a prolonged holiday with pay. The only thing guaranteed to upset Jack was to load the parcels in the wrong order, even one out of sequence would cause him to revert to his native tongue to express himself better.

"Method boyo, y' must 'ave method bach. Make no mistake now, method is best, remember that."

I learned a lot about method with Jack. It's worked ever since and it certainly worked for us. The load slipped away like magic, then, with the main shopping centre done we would wend our way with infinite leisure round the back streets to deliver the remainder. With the round done we would sit on our high seats and wend our way in lordly fashion to the old railway carriage which served as our lunchroom at the stables. Being the only boy at the station, I must admit the drivers spoilt me and though I was christened a 'Buggeroo' any scoldings were rarely other than good natured. Only once did I get into real trouble and that was on a bitterly cold November day.

Actually I thought I was doing them a favour. I noticed as I entered the carriage, after watering Dolly, that Mr Kenyon, a fervent local Evangelist, was at the far end of the carriage, spouting as usual about God and Damnation.

These fellows came, uninvited, almost every day to sermonise whilst the men were having their dinner. Why the drivers put up with them I have never fathomed out, but they did. Even though nobody listened they still turned up with the regularity of rent men. I suppose they meant well, but even I knew they were flogging a dead horse. Most of us were too concerned about this world to worry too much about the next. This particular day, with the devil apparently having a helluva time, Old Kenyon was really giving it some stick, amid a fug you could cut as the stove vied with cigarette smoke to choke us all.

Gerry sat opposite to Jack as we sipped our cocoa. Next to him, greying head resting on his hand as he leaned wearily on the table, sat Harry Birkett, his forehead deeply scarred by a shrapnel wound received on the Somme. Now and then it played him up. It was doing so today.

"Jesus," he muttered, half to himself, "I wish Kenyon'd purra bloody sock in it. It's enough t' make y' turn flamin' atheist."

"Give y' the flamin' willies," grumbled Gerry.

"I don't wish 'im no 'arm," replied Harry, raising his head painfully, "But I wish 'ed jump in the bloody dock."

"Shall I tell 'im?" suggested Gerry. Harry's voice took on a note of alarm.

"No, no, you'll only 'urt 'is feelin's. Y'know warr'es like."

I felt heart sorry for him. He had a big round to do after dinner. Suddenly I had a bright idea, and without delving into it too deeply, rose to put it into operation.

"Where's y' goiin?" stuttered Jack as his cigarette smoke went down the wrong way.

"I'm gonna shift Kenyon." His watery eyes opened in surprise. " 'ow?" he said. I winked. "You'll see," and without further explanation I was gone.

I nipped quickly into the stables opposite, stuffed one of Dolly's old feed bags with wet straw, then back across the yard, on to the carriage roof and gleefully knelt down by the chimney. Seconds later the smoke vanished as I stuffed the bag of straw over it then sat back on the slippery roof to await results. They weren't long in coming. A human avalanche came tumbling out, clutching their throats and gasping for air. It was even better than I expected. Old Kenyon sagged against the stable wall coughing his heart out. Gerry was the first to spot me.

"Come off there y' young sod," he gasped. I slid down the roof with alacrity. Jack too wanted to say something desperately as he clutched the carriage for support. Harry, leaning against the stable wall alongside Mr Kenyon, head tightly clasped in both hands, gazed up at me with homicidal fury. All around us, the other occupants, in various stages of asphixiation, wheezed and gasped as they fought for breath. I was appalled by what I had done, yet deep down I was bursting to laugh, but daren't. At last Gerry got his breath back, grabbed me and shook me like a rat.

"What the 'ell d'y' think y' doin'?" he gasped, eyes running with tears. Before I could answer, Jack, his face cherry red with coughing, shook his stump at me.

"Come by 'ere boyo," he said ominously, "I wanna word with y'." I felt safer hiding behind Gerry.

"What the bloody 'ell did y' do that for?" demanded Harry, still holding his head as smoke belched from the carriage.

"I wanted t' get rid of Kenyon for y'," I said, with a hint of reproach.

"Mother'f God," he gasped, "I'd sooner listen t' 'im than choke t' death. Now get that bloody feed bag off an' open all the doors and winders. It'll stink for a week will that."

He was right, despite all my efforts it still smelt smokey at dinner time the next day but it did stop me from interfering with the Evangelists again. When the going got rough I used to go and sit in the stable with Dolly, at least she didn't preach at me. In any case it was pointless me listening to them. As a fully paid up member of the Papal Light Infantry, I was, according to our lot, already saved, so why bother? Apart from that one incident to upset the normally high spirits of the parcels gang, the only other upset I had was on the occasion when Dolly's normally monumental calm was badly upset and she bolted.

I had seen cowboy films, but never dreamed that I too

would one day be aboard a runaway wagon, not on the open prairie, but up the main shopping centre. It all happened quite innocently on a blustery day about a fortnight after the carriage incident. Jack, having taught me over the weeks how to handle the reins, had let me drive the wagon to the next delivery a few yards up the street while he popped into the tobacconists. On these occasions I always felt pretty important and sat on the high seat with all the airs and graces I could muster.

Dolly responded to my impressive 'Gee Up' and had just settled into her stride when a newspaper lad, riding towards us on the opposite side, fell off his bike. Suddenly the road was full of flying paper. Her ears cocked in fright, then disaster struck. A fluttering paper, fully opened by the wind, struck her forelegs. She reared wildly, whinnying in terror. Next moment she was off. The street was packed with weekend traffic. Pandemonium broke out as she picked up speed and the van began to sway violently. With hair standing on end I wrestled frantically with the reins as they came alive in my hands. I did everything except whistle Annie Laurie. I stood on the brakes, danced on the seat, hauled like hell and screamed blue murder, but all to no avail. She had her head and by the looks on the startled faces flashing past, I was a goner. The cross roads at the top of the shopping centre loomed up. I shuddered at the thought of belting across there at a full gallop with traffic coming from all directions. People screamed, horns blew, other horses reared in fright as we shot past them. With less than fifty yards to go, my eyes dilated with terror, arms aching from the strain, fate took a hand. She slipped. With legs splayed and screaming in terror as the weight of the van pushed her forwards, we gradually slowed, then stopped. Limp with fright I barely remembered being helped down until Jack's voice cascaded over me as his arm went round my shoulders.

"Are y' alright boyo?" he asked anxiously. Without waiting for an answer he went down on his knees to Dolly. In a soothing, lilting voice, he calmed her as no one else could and all the while his rough hand smoothed her glistening coat with gentle stroking movements.

Filled with remorse I knelt beside him. I didn't know what to say as the crowd milled anxiously around us. I knew how much he thought of her. If anything had happened to make them put her down, I think I would have broken my heart. He turned and looked at me.

"Alright bach," he said with unbelievable gentleness, "Don't take on now. It wasn't your fault. I saw the papers fly."

"Will she be alright?" I asked anxiously as Dolly, her hind legs buckled beneath her, eyes rolling pitiously, lay helpless between the shafts.

"Aye, she'll be alright. Nothin's broke as far as I can see. Go on now boyo, nip across t' Molloy's an' get y'self a cuppa tea. It'll calm y', you've 'ad a terrible fright, I know that."

I looked across at Molloy's cafe a few yards away. I couldn't have gone for a fiver. I wanted to see Doll on her feet again. He nodded understandingly as I refused to move.

"Alright then, give me a hand to unshackle her then."

By this time the police had arrived and got things organised. With three willing helpers we got the harness unbuckled in jig time, and with Jack's soft voice in her ear the whole time, they finally got her to her feet. For a few moments he stood her perfectly still and, still talking gently, ran his hands expertly over her. The rolling eyes calmed, the flaring nostrils quietened as she nuzzled him affectionately.

"Hold her Li," he said quietly, "Talk to 'er while I make sure."

With infinite care he examined her legs as I held the bridle and rubbed her nose. At last he stood up with a grin.

"Is she alright?" I asked anxiously.

"Aye boyo, she's fine now, but she'll work no more t'day."

With the help of volunteers he shafted her up more gently than I had ever seen him handle her then, quietly he coaxed her into motion.

"Home my lovely," he said gently, "Steady as y' go."

We sat on the box together. Occasionally I stole a glance at the rough man beside me and wondered at the depth of his gentleness.

10

Pastures New

1936 had started well, and with Christmas rapidly approaching and everyone working for the first time in my memory, it looked as though it would end well too. For me, with a series of peaks and troughs, it had been a Pilgrim's Progress sort of a year. First the euphoria of working in the Yard, then the terrible accident, followed by a new peak as Dad and I drew closer. My unbelievable luck in starting on the railways, and the happy world it had opened for me. It was all so incredible and yet, through it all ran a skein of sadness, as my other world, the 'Gang', slowly disintegrated around me.

Henry and Tommy had gone to their new worlds. Fatty was dead. Sniffer was up to his eyeballs in trouble. Dinny, like a knight after the Holy Grail, chased girls with a single mindedness that left him bug-eyed and shaking with fatigue. Even Bonko Armfield, as thick as two short planks, had caught the 'Judy Bug' and was now, within a week of Christmas, in a besotted, glassy-eyed state with his new amour, Maggie Spencer. We all knew her well from school days, a fine strapping girl with a chest like a ship's fender. As Dinny said sarcastically, 'No one would ever slam a door in her face'. They say that love is blind. Bonko must have had his eyes bricked up. She was twice his size and when she spoke it was a command. Still, why should I worry? That was his funeral. I had my own love, Dolly, now fully recovered from her fall. At least she didn't answer back or cost good money to take to a dance. Despite all, with the Christmas rush in full swing, and the tips coming in steadily, it looked as though a memorable 1936 would end on a high note, just how high I did not realise until I returned home on the Tuesday before Christmas when Mam sprang a surprise that left me gasping.

I could feel there was something on her mind as she hovered and fretted whilst I washed at the sink and then sat down and wolfed the food laid before me.

"How long'll y' be?" she asked, a hint of impatience in her voice. I looked at her closely. Obviously I hadn't done anything wrong, I knew her tone and expressions too well for that.

"Why, what's up?" I asked in a puzzled tone.

"Never mind that," she answered impatiently, "Just 'urry up an' get that down y', I've gotta surprise for y'."

"Hey?"

"Shurrup an' finish y' dinner or they'll be closed."

I gazed at her in astonishment but, without further questions, raced through the rest of the food and gulped down a cup of tea.

"Y' finished?" she demanded. I nodded and rose from the table that now boasted a table cloth for all meals and not just Sunday tea.

"Right," she snapped, "Come on then, we've gotta meet y' Dad outside Taylor's."

I felt a sudden surge of excitement. Taylor's was one of the biggest clothes shops in the town and one of the stores that dealt with 'Cheques', a system without which the poorer classes would never have been clothed at all in the bad times. These, a primitive form of hire purchase, were extremely simple. The firm's representative, or 'Tallyman', would issue a voucher for anything from one pound to a maximum of ten pounds for which repayments could be made at so much a week. The trick for the 'Tallyman' was to get the money back after the cheque was spent. The ten pound ones were of course almost as rare as money itself on our district, where unemployment was endemic. The usual amount was for about two pounds ten shillings, or, if the customer was reliable, anything up to a fiver. The system fitted in very nicely with the pawnshop trade which depended of course on having something to pawn, but that's another, and harrowing story.

"You gorra cheque?" I said excitedly, visualising a new pair of boots or something. She turned as she threw her outdoor shawl over her shoulders.

"Never you mind," she said with a twinkle in her eye, "Just get y' coat on, y' Dad'll tell y'."

I couldn't get out of the house fast enough. Within ten minutes we were outside the shop where Dad, still in his overalls, waited for us. He grinned.

"In y' get," he said without further explanation. I quivered with suppressed excitement as we joined the throng in the warm interior. Without a word they took me upstairs to the Men's Department. Dad pointed to the rows of suits hanging on moveable stands.

" 'ow would y' like wanna them?" he said, watching me closely. I stared at him speechless. A suit, for *me*? I had never worn anything but odds and sods and cut-me-downs all my life. The only new things I had ever had were the odd gansey, boots or clogs and the last of those was two years ago. Even my socks were home made from un-picked wool.

"But . . ." I gasped.

"Go on," he said, " 'ave a look. Nothin' daft now," he warned. I looked at Mam for confirmation. She laughed.

"Go on Li, we're not kiddin'."

I turned to the rack. The assistant gingerly helped me off with my battered coat. How can one describe such a moment? Only Henry of all the gang had ever had a new suit and that was only because he was going away to be a priest. Even Tom only had a second hand one to join the Army, and now here I was surrounded by them. I felt like grabbing the first one that came to hand and getting to hell out of the place before I woke up. But it was no dream. Like a ship in the Basin I was to be 'rigged' out, and Mam saw to it that it was just right. Half a dozen times I went into the nearby cubicle to try them on before she finally gave me the nod. I can still see it in all its glory, a brown, double breasted suit, with a faint herring bone pattern, at the enormous cost of two pounds ten shillings. But that wasn't the end, I was only 'Half Rigged'. The assistant, more obsequious than the one who had served me in the grocer's a few years before when I had taken our family food ticket in exchange for groceries, ushered me gently towards the shirts, two shillings and eleven pence, ties, one shilling, shoes, five shillings and eleven pence, underpants, the first I had ever worn, one shilling and sixpence, singlet, again a stunning first, one shilling and sixpence, socks, a natty brown with white spots, nine pence. I even got a handkerchief of all things, to put in my top pocket. It was an incredible experience.

I watched goggle-eyed as Dad took out of his overall pocket a piece of carefully folded white paper and spread it confidently on the counter. Curious, and clutching the precious bundle tightly I leaned forward and peered at it.

"What's that?" he laughed.

"Take a good look at it Li, it'll be a long time before y' see another one. That's a fiver."

What a night! I walked from the shop in a dream. In less than two months I would be sixteen. I had not only got my first suit but had actually seen a genuine fiver! We had come a long way from the seven and a tanner food ticket.

I was dying to get it on, and the three days to Christmas, the magic morning when I could wear it for public showing, seemed an eternity away but, if I couldn't wear it I was damned if I was going to keep it to myself. Within minutes of arriving home I was off again. Dinny was the first to know, I caught him on his way out with his latest. She quickly got the elbow and he came back with me to admire it. Next day I had my leg pulled unmercifully by my mates in the parcel's hall. At home, the ensemble, now cocooned under an old shirt and hanging on the back of Mam's bedroom door, made interminable journeys as relatives arrived and were at once button-holed by me. Then the great day arrived. I would have been ready for a six o'clock Mass if they had had one. If pride is a sin then

God help me, the Devil had me firmly in his grip as I walked, head high, down the aisle to Communion. Even my shoes squeaked with commendable noise to announce my arrival and departure from the altar. Technically I should have been in a state of grace after receiving the Host, but to my eternal shame I was actually in a state of euphoria.

From church I visited each relative in turn. I must have been absolutely insufferable, sitting on the edge of chairs, pulling my trouser knees up as I had watched the toffs do in the pictures. I was so far gone at Aunt Min's I even tried to drink a cup of tea with my little finger stuck out, but she didn't laugh. She understood.

On Boxing day, exhausted after walking my feet off around town so that as many as possible could see my finery, another bombshell hit me as I walked through the door. The parlour was packed and Mam's face was solemn as I caught the tail end of the conversation.

"Where the 'ell are we gonna put 'er?" she asked.

"God knows," answered Dad from the far side of the room, "She can't stay 'ere, an' that's a fact. Warrabout your Min's?"

"She's got lodgers," broke in Bernadette, my eldest sister.

"Well," said Mam wearily, "There's only one way, Con'll 'ave t' sleep with Liam, an' Teresa will 'ave t' take 'is room." I groaned as all eyes turned to me. Jimmy, my brother-in-law, despite having seen me dressed up a dozen times, rose to the occasion and cheered me up.

"Hell's bells," he cried, as though seeing me for the first time, " 'e looks a right swell doesn't 'e?"

" 'ave y' spilt anythin' on them?" asked Mam anxiously. I shook my head then changed the conversation.

"Is our Teresa comin' 'ome?"

"Yeah, you'll 'ave t' bunk in with Con." I groaned anew. "Ah, Mam."

"It's no good ah Mam'n me. What else can we do with 'er? . . . 'ang 'er in the cupboard?"

"What's she comin' 'ome for?" I asked peevishly. I loved

133

my sister, but her coming meant a major upheaval and I didn't fancy sharing the parlour with Con again. I had had enough of that while I was at school, he kicked like a mule in his sleep.

"She's fed up that's why," said Dad irritably. "Where else would she come when she's fed up but 'ome. Anyroad its none'v your business, so shurrup."

Teresa had been in Dublin almost four years now and, except for occasional visits when she usually slept at Aunt Min's, I had rarely seen her. Now, with the prospect of sleeping on the horsehair couch, backed up with a couple of chairs to make it a double bed, I resented her coming. I was still brooding when a knock came to the back door followed by the ritual 'Coo . . ey'.

"In 'ere Maggie," shouted Mam at the familiar sound of Mrs Bloomfield's voice. Seconds later, Ma Bloomfield who kept the lodging house at the top of the street, waddled in.

"Jesus," she exclaimed, easing her enormous bulk into a protesting chair, "Two steps these days an' I' can't get me bloody wind."

Dad grinned, "It's the thick twist y' keep smokin' Maggie, I tell y' it's no good for y' luv."

"Thick twist?" she said with a wheezy laugh as she hitched her bosom, "More like flamin' old age . . . Anyroad, never mind that, what's all this I 'ear about your Teresa comin' 'ome?" Mam looked at her in astonishment.

" 'ow the 'ell did y' know that? We only 'eard ourselves an hour ago." Ma grinned.

"Did y' ever know anythin' t' 'appen round 'ere I didn't know about?"

"Y' not kiddin'," said Mam, "Y' better than the Birken'ead News."

"It's gonna be a bit awkward for y' with 'im grown up isn't it?" she flicked her head towards me.

"Yeah" said Dad, "Bloody awkward. That's what we've just bin talkin' about. 'ave you any room Maggie?" Mam almost snapped his head off.

"She's not goin' up there even if we all 'ave t' stand up an' make room for 'er." She caught the look on Ma's face. "Nothin' against you Maggie, but you've got some rum fellers up there, an' you know it." Ma grinned amiably. Her house was more like an Irish transit camp than anything else, and the contraband that went through it from the docks was nobody's business.

"I suppose y' right Pat. She's a pretty girl an' I can't keep me eye on all of 'em."

"Warrabout movin' to a bigger 'ouse?" suggested Jimmy, out of the blue.

"Move," cried Bernadette, in astonishment, "Me Mam doesn't wanna move . . . Do y' Mam?"

"Never crossed me mind. I wouldn't mind though . . . but where?"

Ma eased herself forward excitedly.

"Now there's a coincidence! I know where there's a good place goin' . . . well in a coupla weeks anyroad."

"Where?" asked Dad.

"Park Grove."

Even I gasped as she mentioned the name. It was less than a mile away but as far as we were concerned it might just as well have been on the other side of the moon. Facing the Park in a wide sedate road, it was in an area we had always considered the 'Toffs' quarter. True, it was a bit run down from the days when servants crowded the place in their neat uniforms, but the red brick Victorian houses were large and, to us, still had that indefinable air of elegance. In effect, it was out of our class. Dad confirmed my view.

"Ah, come off it Maggie, pull the other one will y', its got bells on."

"Whaddy y' mean?" she cried, "Y' want more room don't y'? Well there's an 'ell of a lot more room there than 'ere, an' that's a fact."

"Y'know what 'e means Maggie," broke in Mam, "They're not for the likes of us."

Jimmy, an ardent socialist, was on his feet in a flash.

"Why the 'ell not?" he demanded, "We're as good as they are aren't we?"

"Alright Jim," said Dad jocularly, "Keep y' shirt on. It's only an idea. Whaddy you think luv?" he added, turning to Mam.

"We couldn't afford it."

"Why not?" snapped Maggie, "They're all workin' aren't they? The rent's not all that much.

"Hey, 'ang on a minute," broke in Jimmy, a glint in his eye, "Why can't we share it?"

"Share it?" exclaimed Mam and Dad together.

"Yeah, why not? We'll need more space in a coupla months. He nodded towards Bernadette now nearing her time with their second child. Maggie slapped her ample thigh.

"Now that's what I call a bloody good idea! Wattabout it Mary?"

Mam looked from one to the other uncertainly.

" 'ow would we furnish it?"

"Look luv, let's cross the bridges when we come to 'em eh? What d'y' think of the idea?

"Oh come on Mam," pleaded Bernadette, "It'll solve everything."

"Just sleep on it for a coupla days," suggested Maggie. "I'll nose around a bit an' see what's goin' on, 'ow's that?"

Mam nodded then looked across at me standing open mouthed at the sudden turn of events.

"Not a word," she said menacingly, "If this gets out I'll scalp y', understand?"

Bursting with excitement at the mere thought of living among the toffs, I felt cheated, I wanted to tell everybody, especially Dinny, but I daren't, yet somehow, and within twenty four hours, I knew it would be around. MI5 had nothing on the intelligence service in our district.

By Saturday, after much mysterious comings and goings between Maggie, Bernadette and every relative within hailing distance, the deal was done and Aunt Min, the only one, by virtue of her steady pension and quiet tastes, who had a coat in addition to the usual shawl, lent it to Mam for her visit to the landlord.

To me she looked strange without the shawl I had known so long, but it suited her down to the ground, even though she did feel uncomfortable in it. For the two hours she was away we waited breathlessly, but the moment she stepped through the door I knew it was ours. What I didn't know then, was that from that moment my whole life would change completely, not overnight of course, but change it would, in ways I never dreamed of.

Our first visit, when it became empty two weeks later, must have seemed like a latter day flight of the Israelites from Egypt. Every relative we had came to inspect it. For me it was fantastic, not only was there a garden in the front, but it had a backyard big enough to play football in. Inside, the ten rooms seemed never ending. The hallway itself seemed twice as big as the kitchen in which we had lived so long, but the room that fascinated me most was the bathroom. Imagine, a whole room just to get washed in! It seemed a helluva waste, but oh, how lovely. I just couldn't wait to get into that gleaming oblong basin, and that wasn't all. In the same room there was also a lavatory. No more tearing down the yard in freezing weather when one was caught short. No more irate shouts of " 'urry up down there I'm waitin'," because there was also one in the yard. Two lavs, it just couldn't be true! God, it would be worth having the 'runs' just to visit them in turn.

I spent the whole of that first Saturday afternoon just wandering in and out of the rooms, switching the new electricity on and off until Mam got mad and clipped me over the ear.

"Stop y' flamin' wanderin' will y', y' makin' me dizzy. Go on, gerrout, if y' can't 'elp, don't 'inder." I wandered out into the yard and straight into a vision.

At first I didn't notice anything as I wandered slowly down the length of the yard, examining the two foot wide strip of garden that ran down one side. I was almost at the bottom when I caught a movement on my right. I looked up into the calm brown eyes of a girl about my own age. I flushed scarlet as the steady eyes examined me from head to foot, then the elegant nose sniffed gently.

" 'ullo," I said gruffly. She smiled but said nothing.

"Yeh deaf?" I asked diplomatically. She shook her head slowly from side to side.

"No," she said, in a polite melodious voice, "I am not deaf . . . nor am I rude," she added with a slight grimace. If she had been a lad I'd have thumped her. Instead I glowered.

"Are you moving in?" she asked, a note of apprehension in her voice.

"Yeah, any objections?" I snapped. She made me feel uncomfortable. I had never met anyone like her before. All the girls I knew could more than hold their own in a slanging match, but all she did was smile. How the hell could you fight a smile?

"No," she said politely, "I have no objections. Why should I? If you want to live here that is your privilege." There was no answer to that one so I glowered again. Without moving a muscle she made me feel like a worm and, as always, I lashed out viciously.

"Toffy nosed sod," I muttered.

"Pardon?"

The words quivered on my lips again but fortunately Mam's voice stopped me.

"Liam."

"Yeah?"

"Come on, I've gorra job for y'." I turned to go but the vision stopped me.

"Who is that lady?"

"That's me Mam," I said grudgingly, "An' that's me Dad," I added as he appeared at the back door.

"And you are . . .?" she added.

"Liam . . . y' just 'eard 'er didn't y'?"

She waited a second or two then raised her pencil thin eyebrows.

"Don't you want to know my name?" she asked. I was dying to know but she made me feel uncomfortable.

"Why should I?" I snapped, "It's no skin off my nose."

A smile quivered on the bow shaped lips as I scuffed the ground with my toe. She was so self assured I could have kicked her.

"Well?" she said quietly.

"Well what?" I snapped as the situation slipped out of my control.

"Well aren't you going to ask? Surely you would want to know my name if we are to live next door to each other. It would be rather strange if we didn't know each other's names, don't you agree?"

God how I wished I was back among my own kind in the street. I knew how to handle girls there, but this one, she made me feel a flaming idiot. I took refuge in belligerence.

"Oh alright then, it's somethin' daft I'll bet."

"Antoinette," she said primly. She coloured slightly as I burst out laughing, then flicked her long hair expertly back over her shoulder.

"Aunty what?" I guffawed. Eyes glinting dangerously she stood her ground as she repeated it, then with a sarcastic sniff she flattened me.

"But there," she added with a faint sniff, "I suppose you are used to Flossies, Maggies, Bellas and such like aren't you?"

I was about to give her an earful when she turned on her dainty heel, and with an elegant toss of her head, cut me deader than a mackerel. I watched her, open mouthed, as she stalked, hips swaying seductively, serenely to her door. She turned with the door half open, gazed at me for a second then, with a final flick of her head, vanished. Fuming, I gazed at the empty space, then stalked into the house in a flaming temper.

"What's up with you?" asked Mam as I slammed the door behind me, "You've gorra face like a farmer's arse on a frosty mornin'." Before I could answer she stuck a bucket in my hand and nodded towards the stairs. "Go an' give y' father an 'and upstairs."

All afternoon, alternating between temper and unexplainable restlessness, I had visions of that calm, superior, oval face framed in a cascade of blue-black hair. I didn't know it, but the 'Judy bug' had caught up with me and only the tremendous pace of work to get the house in living order prevented me pining away on the spot. It was murder. Time and again during odd periods of inactivity between jobs I was jerked from distant scenes of heroic deeds, wherewith to impress my new love, by Mam's stentorian voice.

"Li, what the 'ell's up with y'? . . . Don't stand there like a stuffed dummy . . . Come on lad, there's work t' be done." Then, with darkness falling, she gave me her final order.

"Right," she snapped as she sat down to a cup of tea, "Get upstairs an' 'ave a bath."

For a split second I looked at her puzzled. It was only Tuesday, I wasn't due for the ritual 'all over' until Friday.

"Yeh what?"

"What's up with y'?" demanded Dad, "Y' gone deaf or sumthin'? Y' mother said gerra bath, so move it," I turned to go. "D'y' know 'ow t' work the geyser?"

I shook my head, I had never even seen one before, let alone used one. Mam looked at him anxiously.

"Don't y' think you'd berra show 'im? I don't want 'im blowin' the flamin' place up."

Dad laughed. "Ah don't be daft woman. All 'es gorra do is turn the knob. God 'es not that daft surely?"

"Which one?" I asked. "There's two knobs. I had had a good look at it when I went to inaugurate the loo earlier on.

"The black one y' fool," he snapped impatiently, "Y' worked in the Yard long enough t' know red's for danger didn't y'?"

"What'll 'appen if I turn the red one?" I asked perversely.

"Don't," he snapped, "Now git." I didn't push the question and with these scanty instructions headed for the new world at the head of the stairs.

As I walked through the door to take my first 'starkers'

bath, Dad's voice roared up the stairs, "An' don't forget t' put the plug in or you'll lose the 'ot water."

I closed the door, slipped the catch then sat on the lavatory seat and gazed about me. A bathroom today is almost mandatory, but not then, and this was actually bigger than our old kitchen. Apart from my temporary seat, it had a basin with a little cabinet over it, and over the bath was an enormous copper geyser, bubbling and gurgling like a metallic monster. An unshaded electric light in the centre of the room cast its hard light on the room's final claim to elysian gentility, the wallpaper or, to be more exact, the vertical garden. Flowers, trees, and branches full of exotic birds all the colours of the rainbow, curled and twisted in every direction. For a full five minutes I sat spellbound by the luxury of it all, then, with the plug safely in, I resisted an overwhelming desire to turn the red knob and cautiously turned the black one. Two full turns and I staggered back in alarm as the thing gurgled ominously. Twice I nearly took to my heels as it banged dangerously then to my relief the water began to flow. Triumphantly I turned the knob further and further to increase it and within minutes the room was filled with a steaming fog. With growing confidence I turned the cold water tap, fitted on to the bath itself, to cool it a little as I divested myself of my clothes. At last all was ready for the supreme moment. With the bath three quarters full I stepped in and sat down in one movement. A split second later I came out like a rocketing pheasant as the red hot water clawed at me. I grabbed for the side to steady myself, slipped, then cried in agony as I went under, causing a tidal wave that swept the floor. Within seconds feet pounded on the stairs as the family galloped to the rescue. Hands, accompanied by anxious voices, pounded on the door.

"Are y' alright?" . . . "What's appened?" . . . "Is the geyser alright?"

I daren't let them in before I had cleared the mess up. Holding my steaming backside I shouted a black lie.

"I'm alright. I just burnt me whatsit that's all. The water's a bit 'ot."

"Silly sod," opined Dad from the other side, "Why didn't y' test it first? Put some cold in before y' gerrin again."

"I'll be alright," I assured them, turning the cold tap on again for confirmation. The footsteps receded. With the water cooled I tested it gingerly with my foot, then stepped in. God, the luxury. It was sheer heaven as I sank to my neck and gazed rapturously through the swirling mists at the galaxy of flowers around me. No more 'strip downs' with carbolic soap on freezing nights. No more Mam coming in to examine my neck for tide marks. This was the life and no mistake.

How long I lay in supreme happiness I do not know, but the next thing I remember was a frenzied banging on the door and a babble of voices.

"What's goin' on there?" yelled Dad, "Y' fell down the flamin' plug 'ole or somethin'?"

"D'y' know what time it is?" shouted Mam.

I opened my eyes and felt suddenly chilled. The bath was empty. Slipping and struggling I got to my feet, then, with one foot out of the bath, the door suddenly burst open as Dad finally put his shoulder to it and a human avalanche came tumbling in.

"Mother'v God," exclaimed Mam as she surveyed the wet floor, "What y' bin doin'? Launchin' a bloody ship?"

Holding a towel to hide my nakedness I gazed at her miserably.

"I fell asleep," I said lamely.

"Of all the flamin' eejits" exploded Dad, "Y' 'aven't got enough bloody sense t' come in outa the rain. What's up with y' anyroad?"

"Ah leave 'im alone Dad," broke in Con, " 'es never bin in a bath before y'know. It's easy done. 'e'll get used to it." I looked at him gratefully as Dad grinned.

"Alright then," he said, "But next time y' wanna drown y'self, jump in the river will y'. It doesn't make as much mess . . . Come on," he added, shooing them out of the room, "Lerr'im get dressed. I'll bet 'e won't do that again in a hurry."

He was right, I didn't, but for the next six months I must have been one of the cleanest lads on Merseyside. Rarely a day went by that I didn't take a bath, nor did a day go by that I didn't think of a thousand surreptitious ways to see Antoinette. I rarely spoke to her, I was too tongue-tied, but I watched her, lay in wait to see her, or accidently on purpose met her as she came home from the Convent school or shopping for her mother. I had it bad and it wouldn't go away. On one of the rare occasions I met Dinny, nowadays I asked his advice. Forthright as always he gave it.

"Gerrin there son an' gerrat it. If y' wanna Judy, you've gorra lerrem know 'oose boss mate." He didn't understand Antoinette anymore than I did. God I wished I was educated like her. I wished I could speak properly, I wished . . . I wished.

11

Fish Nor Fowl

In distance we moved one short mile, in outlook we moved a thousand. The change was quiet but definite. Mam's shawl, which I had known from childhood was replaced by a coat. Dad's suit, for so long the property of 'Uncle', now stayed at home. Con, always clean and neat by nature, now wore a collar in the evenings instead of the regulation muffler. Even Seamus, my sturdy four year old nephew played in the garden, not the street, as I had. There was no question, we had definitely 'progressed', even the language changed. Everyone still swore of course, but it had lost its edge and frequency as natures calmed under the beneficent effects of regular work and less worry.

The thing that pleased me most of all was, perhaps by today's standards, almost laughable in its simplicity, and it occurred within a month of our moving. Mam and Dad actually went to the theatre together, first as a special treat from the herculean work they had put in on the house, then, under the family's urgings, it had become a regular Saturday night routine. Never, as long as I could remember, had she left the house except to visit relatives, lay someone out, attend the sick, or go to Mass. The rest of her time was spent working at a thousand different tasks which often took her far into the night. The move liberated her and I thanked God for it. It not only gave me a new home, a new outlook on life, but new parents. Where I fitted in in all this I was not quite sure. Between Antoinette, with her liquid brown eyes disturbing both my sleep and my daily routines, my fanatical desire to wear my one and only suit on every possible occasion, and a growing jealousy of the lads born and bred in my new district, in whose easy going and articulate company I felt tongue-tied and gouche, I was in a permanent flat spin. All the skills of survival that I had learned in the streets seemed useless in this new environment, where words, not fists, seemed to hold sway. With the shrouds of the slums still strongly about me, I felt neither fish, nor fowl, nor good red herring and I wriggled restlessly in the bonds of my own ignorance. Even Dinny, whom I still met occasionally, seemed a different person. Brother though he was to me, he now seemed, God forgive me, rough and uncouth beside those among whom I now lived.

In my other world, a mile away, I could cope, but here, although pleased, I felt uneasy. For the first time in my life I could not compete on equal terms, especially with the slimy, brilliantined creep who berthed alongside Antoinette and carried her nightschool books, or tennis racket on Sunday afternoons. A tennis racket! I wouldn't be seen dead with one in my hand. For years we had poked fun at the 'fairies' in the park as they swatted the silly ball between them. Toffy nosed sods, prancing about in their white shorts and looking down their noses at the 'scruffs' as we pressed our faces to the railings. In retrospect it was a couple of the most agonising months of my life. I floundered like a swimmer out of his depth. Geared to a way of life that recognised, above all, strength, and flung into one whose strength was words and manners, enmeshed in the agonising trauma of early adolescence, and tormented by near homicidal jealousy of anyone who even looked at Antoinette, I didn't, as Aunt Min would say, 'know my arse from my elbow'. To add insult to injury, my suit, my pride and joy, the one thing that might put me on terms with my rivals, (providing I didn't open my mouth), was still strictly confined to special occasions, Mass, Coronations, introductions to the King, and such like. It was maddening. On the rare occasions I cornered Antoinette I suffered all the agonies of an eloquent mute and could sense the ridicule in which her friends held me, and this

145

made me madder than ever. I don't know where the brilliantined lad is now, but he'll never know just how close he came to not drawing his old age pension.

The first of these agonising sessions took place just a week after I had first seen him carrying her books. I thought, "Right mate, I'll have you, I'll get there before she goes to nightschool." At five minutes to seven I was ready and waiting, peeping through the sitting room curtains. Right on time she came through the door, seconds later, gasping in strangulated nonchalance I burst through the front door to greet her. She smiled and struck me dumb, then, with my mouth still half open, Gunga Din appeared from the house carrying her books. A mile away I would have taken them out of his hands and thumped him, but now I smiled, a sickly smile. God it was hard to be a gent. He gave me a sidelong look, stroked his embryo moustache then spoke in a high pitched voice.

"I say Antoinette," he said with a smirking appraisal of my railway uniform, "Is this your new neighbour?"

The flaming creep! He knew I was. My lips thinned, but being posh he didn't recognise the danger signals.

"You *know* this is Liam," she replied with an edge to her voice, "I introduced you on Sunday . . . remember?"

He sniffed gently and gave his moustache an affectionate stroke.

"Of course! How silly of me," he smirked. Silly, I thought. You're not silly mate, you're a bloody idiot,' I surprised myself. A couple of months before I would have said it. Now that was progress. I think she realised this too, she smiled at me then turned.

"I'm sorry Ernest," she said sweetly, "I've just remembered, I can't go this evening, I have to visit Aunt Jane. The poor dear is not too well you know. Really, I am sorry, but you understand don't you?"

I looked at her boggle-eyed. God; She even told lies nicely, her Aunt Jane lived in Stockport. If that's what education did for you it couldn't be all that bad. He gazed at her horrified.

146

"But Aunt . . ."

"Now don't be tiresome Ernest, you are always telling me that a promise is a promise, isn't that so?" He nodded dumbly.

"But Antoinette" he pleaded as she took the books from his hand.

"You 'eard 'er mate," I said bluntly, "Shove off." He gazed at me malevolently then, without a word, turned on his well clad heel and slouched disconsolately down the path. I looked at her calm unruffled face in admiration. What a way to give the elbow, so neat, so quiet, the Borgias could have taken a lesson.

"That was a flippin' lie an' you know it," I said with my usual diplomacy. She laughed lightly.

"But I do have to visit Aunt Jane, and the poor dear isn't well."

"Yeah but . . ."

"I didn't say when I have to visit did I? So it is not a lie really is it?"

I wasn't up to the ecclesiastical niceties of lying but it suited me. I had her all to myself for at least a mile and a half, to talk to, look at and, who knows, if I worked it right I might even get to hold her hand. Then? . . . The possibilities were endless. It was a night I shall always remember, the sheer ecstasy of just walking with her. I was so far gone I wouldn't have given a damn if it had been a tennis racket I was carrying. After a sleepless night, during which I walked endless Elysian fields, I floated into the station next day in a semi-trance and straight into a serious faced Jack.

"The Gaffer wants t' see y'," he announced flatly. A rapid search of all that I had done over the past week revealed nothing of a punishable nature.

"What's up?" I asked anxiously. He remained solemn.

"Dunno boyo. Gaffer sent a message 'e wants t' see y', that's all I know, so get crackin'."

He nodded towards the holy of holies, the station master's office. Two minutes later I faced the great man, resplendent in his gold braided uniform. I felt a little easier as I gazed up at the tall, austere figure. He had a smile on his face.

"How would you like to be a driver?" he asked abruptly.

"Yeh what?" I replied, astounded.

"A driver, or to be precise, a Junior van driver." I looked at him open mouthed as he lowered himself into his chair and took a slip of paper from a tray.

"You are sixteen aren't you?" I nodded.

"And a bit, Sir."

"Would you like to drive a van?"

What a daft question. My own van, a driver's uniform complete with Pea Jacket and real leather leggings! He might just as well have asked me would I like to be Pope. I nodded in suppressed excitement.

"Oh yes Sir, not 'alf." A smile flickered across his face as he eyed me up and down then, out of the blue he revealed the source of this sudden good fortune.

"Jones tells me that you're a good lad and have worked well since you have been with him. Didn't he tell you that he had recommended you for a course?"

I shook my head dumbly. How could I tell him that it wasn't work but more like a paid holiday with the van men, and Jack in particular. I hadn't even noticed how hard I worked.

"You realise of course," he added sternly, "That it will mean you going away from home for a while to the driving school in Yorkshire?"

Trembling with excitement I nodded. To get hold of a van I would have gone to Timbuktu. He dismissed me and I staggered out straight into a grinning Jack and a bunch of men from the vans.

"Well?" he said.

"I'm gonna go on a course," I spluttered, "A driver's course."

"You cin do it boyo," he said confidently.

"Course 'e can," broke in Gerry, " 'es taken my van up the road many a time. It was true. At every opportunity the motor van drivers let me run their vans up the railway road until we reached the main street, despite regulations.

"When are'y' goin'?" asked Jack, concern on his face for the first time. I shrugged.

" 'e never said. Just asked me if I wanted to go, that's all."

"I reckon 'e'll be off in about two weeks," said Old Harry. He was wrong. Just one week later the moment came for me to leave home for the very first time. In fact, despite our interminable free rides on the Ferry, I had actually only set foot in Liverpool twice in my life and been on a train only once on the memorable fifteen mile journey to Chester but I had never slept away from home, except for one night at Dinny's during the riots. From the fuss that was made in preparation and the advice poured in by the bucketful the night before my departure, one would have thought it was Timbuktu I was journeying to. Even Antoinette, besotted though I was with her, took second place to this new excitement. What a year it had been. First the move, then Antoinette, now this. The week between the interview and departure passed like a day. The Friday night before my six o'clock departure next morning I was restless. For the first time in my life I would be on my own, really on my own. I felt a strange fear, not the fear of danger, I was well used to danger, but a deeper fear as I realised I would not see my family for three whole weeks. What if Mam or Dad took ill? What if I took ill and they weren't within reach? Hell's bells, it didn't bear thinking about. I willed the morning to come, yet somehow dreaded it.

Within minutes of coming down from the bathroom, the family was around me, anxiously firing questions. Was I alright? . . . Did I want to go . . . What I should do if this or that went wrong . . . I mustn't forget to write. Hell, I had never written a letter in my life. What the devil would I talk about in a letter? . . . "Don't forget to be polite to everyone, and for God's sake, don't get inter any trouble will y'? Oh yes, don't forget to go t' Mass, y'know what'll 'appen if y' don't go," (I didn't but didn't intend to take any chances), and finally, "Whatever y' do keep y'self clean."

Captain Scott was no better prepared for the South Pole and of course, before the hour of departure Aunt Sarah arrived. All the previous instructions were run through again plus her own experienced opinion that I was far too young to go away on my own and that Mam would regret it. Dad's answer was blunt and simple.

" 'oly Sailor," he said, " 'es gotta grow up sometime 'asn't 'e?" There was no answer to that one so they shut up. At six sharp they prepared to come to the ferry with me. I was horrified. I pleaded with them not to, it would make me feel daft. All but Dad respected my wishes but it meant a tearful departure from Aunt Min.

My luggage was light for the simple reason I had nothing to pack except a change of underclothes which I had been shown how to wash but not iron, a spare pair of socks and that was it. Under my railway uniform was a new gansey to look respectable in off duty hours and to complete the ensemble, a new tooth brush and tin of toothpaste, neither of which had been opened because from childhood I had followed the age old practice of cleaning my teeth with a mixture of salt and soot rubbed in with the finger. Financially I felt on a par with the Aga Khan. Apart from two shillings in loose change in my pocket I had the greatest sum ever in my possession carefully sewn into the lining of my jacket, two pounds. With this and my free railway ticket I stood on the platform in Lime Street, the complete traveller, nervous, but definitely complete. As the guard's whistle blew I felt tongue-tied and embarrassed as Dad put his hand on my shoulder and looked at me solemnly.

"Do as y' told Li. Get y' 'ead down an' listen t' what y' bein' told. You'll learn it, don't worry." His face softened as I looked up at him. "You'll be alright," he continued, "Y' not daft." He held his calloused hand out as the whistle blew for the second time and the engine screeched in reply.

"Don't forget," he said as he gripped my sweating hand

through the window, "If y' in any kinder trouble go to the nearest priest. Don't listen to anyone else an' you'll be alright. Understand?"

The engine jerked on the first step of its journey. Still holding my hand he walked alongside.

"Y' sure y' alright now?" he yelled above the noise. I nodded miserably as the full portent of the journey hit me and loneliness settled like a cloud. God I wished I wasn't going. I wanted to be with the family. His grip relaxed then broke as the train picked up speed. I leaned out of the window to see him for as long as possible. I can still see him, both arms raised as the train took the first of the gentle curves out of the station and cut his short stocky figure from view. The umbilical cord was cut, and for one frightening moment I felt the same terrible loneliness that had swept me the time, years before, when Mam had been rushed to hospital with appendicitis. The journey itself I have completely forgotten except for the interminable click of the wheels which seemed to go on for hours before we stopped at a rural station.

"Cleckheaton!" roared a broad Yorkshire voice. In a semi daze I grabbed my cheap cardboard suitcase and hurled myself into strange country, then with my free ticket in my hand, made for the ticket collector. Short, very thickset, and with a bullet shaped head bristling with iron grey hair, he made me feel distinctly uncomfortable. For a second or two I stood gazing at him uncertainly.

"Come on lad," he snapped. "Don't stand there gawpin', 'aven't got all day tha knows."

I handed over my ticket with an enquiry as to where the Driving School was.

"Tha's 'ere." I looked at him puzzled as I took the return half back. "There thee daft 'aperth." He pointed to a lonely looking building about half a mile down the track. "There's thos'tel. But what're thee doin' goin' there?" he added in a puzzled tone.

"I'm gonna learn t' drive," I said proudly. His piercing blue eyes opened in surprise.

"Thee, a Driver, thar nobut a kid. What're thar doin' drivin? Thar'll not be safe on road, thee."

"I'm a junior van driver," I said indignantly.

"Junior driver," he exclaimed in disgust, "Wi' good men walkin' streets? What the 'ell are railways comin' t', I ask thee?"

Having heard Archie, Uncle Mick's shipmate, I could just about make out what he was talking about, but only just. I was beginning to get a bit hot under the collar at his disparaging tone. He grinned broadly.

"Ah tak no notice of me lad, it's not thar fault . . . It's them up the're." He jabbed his thumb backwards at some unseen fiends in high places. "Tha's alright, tha'll do well. Na thee listen young'un," he added, coming out of his box and putting his hand on my shoulder. "Tha takes that road there, y' see?" I couldn't but I nodded, "Then tha turns left at 'Plough, then tha's there. Dost understand?"

I didn't have a clue. Dad had slipped up badly. He hadn't told me they were foreigners in Yorkshire. He gave me a friendly pat then shoved me forward. I thanked him and determined to ask the first policeman I saw. He was bound to speak English. I was in luck, less than two hundred yards from the station I met one, pushing his bike. He didn't seem very happy as he flogged it up the steep incline towards the station. I flagged him down. He stopped and gazed at me suspiciously.

"Tha doesn't live 'ere'abouts," he announced accusingly. I groaned. God, another one. I explained who I was and where I was going. He pondered my answer seriously.

"Tha's a young'un t' be travellin' on own aren't thee?" he said, eyes narrowing suspiciously. I was beginning to agree with him but I wanted to go to the toilet and things were getting a bit urgent for detailed discussion. His next question came out of the blue, as he took his note book out of his pocket.

"Dost thar mother know tha's 'ere?" I looked at him in amazement.

"Course she does," I exclaimed indignantly, "So does

152

me Dad." He looked relieved and returned his note book.
"I told y', I'm gonna be a driver."

"Right," he announced, turning his bike round, "I'll take thee, then I'll know tha's safe." I could have kicked him. In a flash he had taken away my new found independence.

"I'm alri . . ." I began. He cut me short.

"Tha'll do as tha told," he announced authoritatively, "Foller me."

I 'follered' without protest. Evidently he was now in 'loco parentis'. Ten minutes later we were outside the squat, square built hostel where the train drivers and firemen slept overnight when they changed trains. Inside the musty hallway the policeman walloped a little brass bell on the table. A tall, thin, sandy haired man appeared like a Genie. A smile hovered on his lips as he greeted my companion.

"Hello Thomas," he said, in an accent strange to me, "What have we here then?"

I felt like a criminal as I stood between them.

"Says 'es comin' 'ere t' learn t' drive," announced Thomas, a hint of suspicion in his voice. "Just wanted t' make sure lad was safe, tha knows, 'im bein' a stranger an' all." He gave the newcomer a ponderous wink, then added, "Away from 'is Mam for the first time 'e tells me."

"Thomas," said Mr Connolly, the Warden of the hostel, "You get worse as you get older, anyone would think the lad was in mortal danger."

"Aah, lads is lads Mr Connolly sir, an' away from 'ome first time . . . well, tha knows."

Mr Connolly patted me on the shoulder as Thomas turned to go.

"By the way Thomas," he called, "Do you fancy a little er . . ." He waggled his hand in a drinking motion. Thomas shook his head ruefully.

"Not on duty Mr Connolly," he said, regret in his voice, "Good luck t' y' lad," he added as he strode, heavy footed to the door and out into the watery sunshine beyond. Mr Connolly took a piece of paper from his pocket and consulted it. It obviously had my details on it.

"Right Liam," he said, taking my suitcase from me, "Let's get you settled in."

He led me through the hall and up a short flight of uncarpeted stairs. We stopped for a moment at the end of a long corridor with doors down either side. Consulting his paper again we walked a few paces and stopped outside room number four. As he opened the door I gazed into the tiny room that was to be my home for the next three weeks. Actually it was more like a cell than a room. The furnishings were spartan, a chair, half hidden beneath a bare wooden table stood on one side of the room and a couple of paces away on the other side an iron bedstead with a biscuit-thin mattress and three rough army blankets. The three cornered metal washbasin, bolted into the angle of the wall at the foot of the bed, and shining dully against the billious green of the walls, completed the picture of austerity. Not exactly the Waldorf, but a damned sight better than the slums from which I had so recently escaped.

The bathroom and toilets lower down the corridor were communal and the abundant supply of carbolic soap was in constant demand by a succession of drivers and firemen as they came in from their long journeys at all hours of the day and night to catch a few hours sleep before taking fresh trains out. The food, simple but ample, consisted mainly of sausages, bacon, eggs and chips, with a liberal supply of bread and jam if it took one's fancy.

Being the only lad amid a constantly changing population, I was spoilt by a succession of crews whose only idea seemed to be to take Dad's place with advice of all descriptions. Of all the crews, only one man stirred instant dislike in me. It was the first Tuesday of my stay. He button-holed me as I left the canteen after supper with a cup of steaming cocoa in my hand.

"Well hello there," he said in a strange sing song voice, "What y' doin' then?"

"Learnin' t' drive," I said, looking uneasily into the pale oval face with its light blue eyes.

"Oh fancy that now. What a clever little lad. What y' doin' this evenin'?"

"Nuthin'," I said uneasily. He gave me the creeps. He moved closer.

"What about if I come up t' y' room an' 'ave a natter then?"

Suddenly another form materialised alongside me. It was a fireman from another crew.

"Knock it off Charlie," he said sharply, "Or I'll tie a knot in it mate an' ram it down y' gullet."

"I didn't mean nuthin'," said Charlie, alarm in his high pitched voice as he turned and left us. I looked away from my new companion to the rapidly vanishing Charlie

"If I was you lad," he said in a fatherly tone, "I'd keep me 'and on me a'penny when that feller's about, I reckon 'es wanna them!" He gave my hair a quick ruffle, "See yeh."

I looked at the retreating form in blank astonishment. I never saw either of them again and I was over a year in the Army before I eventually cottoned on to what my saviour was going to tie in a knot. If I'd known at the time I'd have screamed blue murder. Apart from that one incident they were among the happiest weeks of my life. Mr Connolly and his wife treated me like the son they had never had. The two pounds I had been given was never spent except on presents to take home, a Toby jug for Mam, a pipe for Dad, (although I had never seen him smoke one in my life). It was going to be a great feeling to give something after this memorable trip.

The course itself was a dream. Every vehicle that the Railways had for parcel delivery was there except one, the actual vehicle I would drive on my job if I passed, a three wheeled James van with a motor-cycle type engine. I didn't care. I could cross that bridge when I came to it. I was in heaven, why bother with trifles?

The instruction was good and the training thorough. I was made to try my hand at everything including an old Ford truck with a gate change outside the cab. I had a hell of a job with that one, but, thank God, it was so slow I could almost leave the enormous wheel, nip on to the running board, change gear and get back behind the wheel before I hit anything. It was fortunate that we never used this on the roads, but everything else we did. On the Friday of the third week I braced myself for the tests. All day, the four adults and myself undergoing the course, alternated between the two railway examiners. Each of us took every vehicle in turn, then at three o'clock the moment I had been dreading arrived, the final test of town driving. I took mine in a small Ford and felt a bit like King Tut as I chugged my way through the narrow streets until finally ordered back. Palpitating with anxiety I applied the brakes outside the office and switched off under the silent gaze of the enigmatic Yorkshire man beside me. Had I passed? When would I know? The melancholy face, its natural sadness enhanced by a tobacco stained walrus moustache, raised slowly. I felt my heart drop as the big brown eyes turned on me, his expression suggested that he had lost a quid and found a tanner, but I was wrong.

"Tha'll do," he said with a slow grin. Ugly as he was I could have kissed him.

The course itself, as it turned out, was not the most important thing on this, my first trip away from home. The hostel, by its very nature, had nothing to offer by way of entertainment but, through the kindness of Mr Connolly and his wife I became part of the family and through them entered a whole new world of books. Mr Connolly, a great reader, gave me the run of his well stocked shelves. At first I baulked, it reminded me too much of school, and with the gang reading had never been a strong point, except for Henry who loved to read. It was sissies stuff.

Within a day or so I weakened under his enthusiasm, within a week I was captivated by the pictures and descriptions in a series of volumes about Africa. He spent hours explaining words I have never seen before. From Africa he introduced me to Hulme's History of England, (well the pictures and captions anyway), by the end of the course I had segs on my eyes from reading, I became enthralled with it. He helped me with my first letter home, the original version being one of the shortest on record, "Hello. I'm here. A lovely train ride. God bless. Write termorrer. Liam." He laughed when he saw it.

"You can't send that lad. You might as well send them a telegram. Your mother and father will be worried about you. They want to know all that you are doing. It's easy, come on, I'll show you."

With his supper forgotten we composed together. Dad's reply showed their surprise at its lucidity. By the end of the first week I no longer dreaded the deluge of mail that came from all members of the family daily. To my surprise I found I began to look forward to it, I was even more surprised to find that I could express myself better on paper to Antoinette than I could speak to her. At this distance I lost all inhibitions that held me tongue-tied in her presence. I found a new confidence. The more I wrote the more I liked it and all the time Mr Connolly encouraged and corrected me, urged me to delve among his books. History was his special love, as indeed it is now mine. He made it live for me as school had never done.

"It is all there at your finger tips lad" he said a hundred times, "Everything you want, if you want it. Travel, science, laughter, anything and everything. You can travel to any part of the world by just picking one up. Imagine that Liam, a whole world at your finger tips, and all you have to do is look." I thought of Antoinette and her self assurance, the clarity with which she could put her views on topics I knew nothing about. He had given me a peep through the magic gates and for the first time I realised I was as thick as a brick. Crafty, yes. Resourceful, yes, we had had to be, but articulate, never.

12

John Barleycorn and I

In the short time that I had been away the house had been transformed. Dad, Con, and Uncle Mat had gone berserk and built, of all things, a greenhouse. How and where they got the wood and glass I never asked, but as soon as I put my case down I was yanked outside to see it. My next surprise came right on its heels. As I walked back into the kitchen a pair of hands clamped over my eyes from behind and a familiar voice cried, "Guess Who?" It was my youngest sister Teresa, home at last from her job in service in Dublin. A split second later we were both in a wild jig around the kitchen. Suddenly the house was full of relatives. Aunt Sarah, solemn as usual, planted a leathery kiss on my cheek and, despite my safe return, opined as she did on the day I left, that she still thought I was too young to be away from home on my own. Aunt Min, round and jolly as ever, was right on cue.

"Aah would y' whisht Sarah, 'es breeched, what more d'y' want? Come on Li luv, give us a kiss."

Good old Aunt Min. Childless herself, she was always a certain refuge for me in good times and bad, even though she did tend to fall asleep at the drop of a hat. I tried to parry a dozen questions at once. "Did y' get inter any trouble?" "No Dad." "Did y' go t' Mass?" "Of course I did Mam." (I wouldn't dare miss.) "Did y' crash the motor?" " 'Course not, d'y' think I'm daft?" Trust Aunt Sarah to look on the black side. "Hasn't he grown!" Service had obviously done my sister good, she didn't even look like dropping her aitches. I felt a sudden tug at my trousers. It was Seamus, my four year old nephew.

"Did y' bring me a present?" The question was quickly followed by a howl as Bernadette's hand connected with his bottom.

"Y' shouldn't ask," she snapped. Seamus looked at her, lips quivering until I swept him into my arms. His eyes gleamed moistly as I reached down, opened the suitcase and extracted the coloured ball I had brought him. Cries of alarm broke out as he wriggled free and headed excitedly for the yard.

"Mind the Green'ouse," roared Dad.

" 'ell purrit straight through the winder you'll see," promised Aunt Sarah. He did.

It was just like the old days in Pleasant Street, all the family together and talking fifty to the dozen as Mam brewed the tea. It was good to be home even though I was made to recount in agonising detail all that had happened to me. I felt safe and secure again. In the world outside I was nothing, here I was surrounded by treasures, noisy, argumentative to be sure, but treasures nonetheless. Even Con, the most reticent of them all, who walked in in the middle of the discourse, gave me a hug of welcome. I felt quite honoured. The two pounds that Mam had so carefully sewn into the lining of my uniform jacket had gone a long way. There was a little something for everyone except Teresa whom I didn't know was home. It wasn't much, but their value was enhanced a thousandfold by the cries of delight which greeted them. I felt good, so good in fact that even Antoinette, who had rarely been out of my thoughts, was momentarily forgotten. Then, within an hour of arriving home came another surprise. In walked Tommy Rolf.

It had been almost two years since I had seen him and I scarcely recognised the burly figure framed in the kitchen doorway, resplendent in his Cavalry uniform and sporting a neat military moustache.

"Hi ya Li?" he said, grinning as I gazed at him dumbfounded. The change was amazing and I felt a twinge of jealousy as I looked at the broad shoulders, the sunburnt face, and the confident practised way he flicked his short swagger stick under his arm as he came forward with outstretched hand. If only Dad had let me join up with him when I wanted to.

" 'ow long've y' bin 'ome?" I queried as he doffed his peaked cap and sat down beside Aunt Min.

"Coupla weeks."

"When are y' goin' back?"

"Termorrer."

I felt a shock of disappointment. After missing him on his last two short leaves I had hoped that we could have had a few days together at last.

"Flippin' 'eck, that's quick isn't it?"

"Well 'es bin 'ome a fortnight," broke in Mam, " 'e came t' see y' as soon as 'e came 'ome, didn't y' Tom?" He nodded.

"Where y' stationed?" I asked, hoping that if he was close enough I might be able to go and see him.

"Nowhere," he answered with a grin, "But I believe I'm goin' somewhere near Hydrabad."

"Y'what? . . . where's that?"

"Y'know . . . India." I looked at him in amazement.

"India! What're they sendin' y' there for?" He shrugged.

"Search me, but that's where I'm goin'. I'm on embarkation leave."

"Where y' goin' from?"

"The Pool," I looked across at Dad for confirmation. He nodded.

"S'right," he said, "The boat leaves Liverpool termorrer night . . . midnight."

Another day and I would have missed him altogether.

" 'e'll be away a long time on this trip an' no mistake."

"Bloody shame," declared Aunt Min vehemently, "Sendin' a kid all that way."

"It's alright Aunt Min," broke in Tom with a laugh, "I *am* a soldier y'know."

"A boy soldier," emphasised Dad, "I agree with 'er, it's a 'elluva long way t' send anyone so young."

"Oh come off it Dad," exclaimed Con, "It's all part of

the life. Besides, 'e laps it up don't y' Tom?" Tom grinned happily.

"Yeah, it's a great life, if y' like it. Anyroad, I'll see the world for nuthin' won't I? And I'm not goin' by meself y'know. We've got one or two 'airy Sergeant majors with us." Aunt Sarah sniffed heavily.

"I don't agree with soldiers," she stated flatly, "We 'ad enough of them in the war, fightin' an' killin' an' God knows what all."

"Oh shurrup Sarah will y'?" snapped Aunt Min. "Soldiers is soldiers an' they go where they're told, isn't that right Tom?" He grinned broadly.

"What does y' Mam think of it Tom?" asked Mam quietly. He shrugged.

"Ah y'know, all Mams worry don't they? But she likes me in uniform."

"An' y' Dad?" asked Aunt Min.

"Oh 'e's all for it. Said it'll broaden me mind y'know. Anyroad, 'e say's there's nuthin' 'ere for me."

" 'e's right there," broke in Con, "Li's bin lucky gerrin' on the railways."

"Warrabout Din?" asked Tom, accepting another cup of tea and looking at me expectantly. I laughed.

"Y'know Din, warrever 'e does 'e lands on 'is feet. I 'aven't seen 'im for months but I think 'es still at the Yard."

"Doin' what?"

" 'es on the weldin' now, isn't 'e Con?" asked Dad. Con nodded.

'Yeah, an' 'ell be a good tradesman if 'e sticks at it." Tom laughed.

"Don't worry, if the money's any good 'e'll stick at it, won't 'e Li? There's no flies on our Din. Hey, by the way, is that right 'es courtin'?"

"Courtin' . . . y' kiddin'. I'll lay ten t' one 'es 'ad a dozen different Judies in the time I've bin away, 'e's a right ladies' man I'll tell y'."

"Where does 'e live now? I was 'oping t' see all the gang before I left this time."

"They've got wanna them there Corporation 'ouses up at the North End, y'know?"

"D'they like it?"

"Well y'know them, don't y'? Last time I was there it was just like the old place, kids fightin', Ma Devlin screamin', y'know?"

"D'yeh reckon we could see Din t'night? I'd like t' see 'im before I sail. In fact I'd like t' see all the lads, I might be away for flippin' years in that place."

"Yeh won't see all the lads Tom."

"Oh I know I won't see 'enry, 'es in College isn't 'e? Imagine, one'f our gang in College, sounds posh doesn't it?"

"Ah God luv 'im," said Aunt Min, "When 'e made that lad 'e made a perfect priest."

Tom and I grinned as we exchanged glances. She didn't know Henry as we did.

"Yeah," I lied, " 'e always was a good un. 'e'll make a good priest."

" 'e will that," agreed Tom, "But warrabout Fatty Boyle? I 'aven't seen 'ide nor 'air of 'im since I came home."

There was a sudden silence in the room. Tom looked round in surprise.

'What's up?" he asked.

"Didn't y' know then?" asked Mam.

"Know what Mrs Sullivan?" She looked across at Dad uncomfortably. He leaned across and tapped Tom's knee.

" 'e was killed down the Yard," he said gently. Tom looked at him in horror.

"Killed? . . . 'ow?"

"Playin' a silly bloody game that's 'ow," snapped Uncle Mat harshly, "Wouldn't be told, any'f 'em." he added with a fierce look at me. "Li knows, 'e was there."

Tom looked at me. I shook my head.

"I'll tell y' about it later," I said uncomfortably. The very memory of that short, fat body hurtling down the hatch made me feel sick. All the happiness of the past couple of hours vanished as the picture seared my mind again. I thought I had forgotten it, but I hadn't. Even now my insides curl at the memory.

"Later Tom, not now. It was an accident that's all."

"Well warrabout Sniffer then? I know 'e got the birch just before I joined up but what 'appened after that?"

"Well y'know the old judge told 'im that it'd be Borstal if 'e ever came up again?"

"Yeah."

"Well 'e wasn't kiddin', 'e stashed 'im away for six months."

"The stupid sod," Tom covered his mouth quickly as he realised where he was, "Sorry Mrs Sullivan, I didn't mea . . ."

"Oh that's alright Tom," she said amiably, "I agree with y', 'e was a silly sod and . . ."

"Now that's not right Mam," exclaimed Con, "It wasn't 'is fault really was it? Those shysters 'e was runnin' with threatened t' do 'im if 'e didn't keep a lookout for them, 'e just got caught that's all."

"What's 'e doin' now then?"

"Gone t' sea."

"Y'what?" ejaculated Tom, "Blimey, 'e used t' get sick on the ferry." Dad laughed.

"I 'ope 'e's got over that then because 'ell 'ave a helluva long time t' be sick now, 'e's on a P&O boat."

"Doin' what?"

"Cabin boy," replied Dad, "the best thing that ever 'appened to 'im. 'e was dead jammy t' gerrit, I'll tell y', especially after bein' inside."

" 'ow come?"

"One'v 'is uncles wangled 'im in. Been a steward for years 'e 'as. Let's 'ope young Johnston sticks it, 'e won't gerranother chance I'll tell y'."

"What 'appened to old Bonko then? Surely 'e's still around?" said Tom, exasperation in his voice.

"Oh 'e's still around alright," said Bernadette with a laugh, " 'e won't move far I cin tell y' . . . Maggie won't lerr'im." Tom looked at me, puzzled, as everyone burst out laughing.

"What's the joke? . . . Don't tell me he's courtin'." he said disbelievingly.

"Courtin'," said Dad, " 'es married."

"Aah come off it, Y' kiddin'?" Mam shook her head sadly.

" 'es not kiddin' Tom, 'e's married alright. 'e 'ad to."

"Had to' 'ell's bells, 'e was scared stiff of girls."

" 'e shoulda stayed that way," opined Uncle Mat with a grin. It was the perfect cue for Aunt Sarah to sniff again. She did so as she rose.

"This is no place for respectable folk," she said stiffly. Uncle Mat looked at her disgustedly.

"Ah for God's sake siddown woman." he snapped "Y' worse'n a flippin' nun. Young Armfield got the girl inter trouble didn't 'e?" he said, looking at her squarely. " 'e 'ad t' get married didn't 'e? So why mince words? Siddown will yeh?"

"Who was it?" asked Tom as Aunt Sarah pursed her thin lips and sat down with her hands primly in her lap.

"You'll never believe it," I said with a grin, "Go on 'ave a guess."

I shook my head as he tried several names in turn then gave up.

"Go on I'll buy it."

"Ma Bloomfield's granddaughter."

"Not Maggie Spencer," he gasped in horror. I nodded. "But she's built like a bus'orse'."

"Yeah, isn't she, but," I added hastily, "She's a nice girl . . . well, y'know?"

"It's a good job," said Tom, still shocked by the news, "There's a lot of 'er."

"Yeah, an' there's even more of 'er now," broke in Con quietly, "She's just 'ad a nipper." Tom looked at him incredulously.

"Bonko a Dad? But 'e's only seventeen? 'ow d . . ."

" 'e shoulda thought of that before." Mam broke off in confusion.

"Hell, I always knew 'e was daft," continued Tom, "But not that daft, it doesn't seem five minutes since we were all at school, never mind bein' married."

"Aye," said Dad soberly, "Time flies Tom, an' it'll fly a damned sight faster the older y' get lad." Tom turned to me.

"Well I dunno Li, I was 'opin t' 'ave a birra fun with the lads before I went back, but there's only you an' Din. What d'y' reckon? D'y' think Din'd come?"

I looked across at Dad. Unlike Tom I was still under the very strict discipline of home. Dad was the boss. Even Con, several years older than I, had to be in on time at night, *dad's* time. I saw him and Mam exchange glances.

"Ah go on," encouraged Aunt Min, "Tom's off termorrer. God knows when they'll see each other again."

I saw him waver. Good old Aunt Min I thought. Mam came unexpectedly to my aid.

"Go on Pat," she said coaxingly, " 'es a man now, not a lad."

"Nearly a man," he answered quietly.

"Go on Mr Sullivan," urged Tom, "We'll be alright, honest."

"Where y' goin'?" Tom and I looked at each other. Neither of us had a clue, but Tom was up to it.

"I thought we'd go an' see Dinny then, if we cin gerrin, we might go to the 'Gyle', second 'ouse," he added quickly. I gave him an admiring glance. That was a good one. The Argyle Theatre, renowned throughout the North for the quality of its acts, was a favourite place of Dad's because he had often worked there doing odd jobs during the bad times to earn a few coppers.

"But that doesn't finish 'til 'alf ten," he said suspiciously, "Why can't y' go t' the first 'ouse. That'll be out by half eight or nine?"

"We've gorra see Din first. Y'know what they're like," I said. He grinned.

"Oh alright then, seein' you've done well on the course, an' Tom's goin' away I'll stretch it this once. I'll give y' 'til eleven o'clock."

I gasped in surprise. Eleven o'clock. I had never been out that late in my life.

"No nonsense," he warned, "Eleven sharp, an' keep outa trouble, understand?"

It was a night I will never forget. It started bad and progressed to complete disaster. Within half an hour, after a quick tour of our house which brought gasps of admiration from Tom, we were on our way. The Devlins were in, in fact half the town seemed to be there as well, it was bedlam. Dinny was delighted. A quick trip round to his latest girl friend to give her the elbow, and we were off. Fifteen minutes later we cornered Bonko in the dilapidated tenement he shared with three other families. God he looked terrible. Maggie, twice his size and as strident as the glassy-eyed child, screaming in her filthy lap, glared at us belligerently. He looked hollow eyed and bemused amid the squalor that one moment of misdirected ecstasy had landed him in. The visit was brief and poignant and we looked at him sympathetically as he came to the head of the stairs to see us off.

"Sorry y' can't come Bonk," said Tom feelingly as the fetid smell of the house wafted around us.

"So am I," he replied savagely, "But she'd scream 'er bloody 'ead off mate if I did."

"Why don't y' tell 'er t' get stuffed?" suggested Dinny, "You're the boss arn't yeh?"

Bonko looked at him forlornly.

"You don't know 'er mate. She's like a bloody fog'orn when she starts. It's bad enough with the kid without 'er startin'. No, you enjoy y'selves. I'll see y' sometime."

Tom shook hands with him solemnly.

"Cheers Bonk. Look after y'self mate, don't lerr'er get y' down son."

We walked into the cobbled street. I could have wept as I turned for a final wave and saw the emaciated figure framed in the peeling doorway. Poor old Bonko, easy going and as daft as a brush since he was a lad, it just didn't seem possible that he was already trapped in the grinding poverty that we had all known so well, Dinny, as always, put it in a nutshell.

"Its 'is own bloody fault, 'e shoulda kept 'is 'and on 'is ha'penny."

Still discussing the sudden downfall of Bonko before he had even begun to live, we arrived at the lengthening queue outside the theatre. The show was supposed to be a good one. Hetty King, the male impersonator, a juggling act, a good comic magician, and the ones I wanted to see above all, Wilson, Kepple and Betty, the pseudo Egyptian Sand Dancers who, for the past week, had kept everybody in stitches. We still had a good half hour to go before the doors opened but the time wasn't wasted. As Dad often said, there were sometimes better turns outside the theatre than in, as a continuous stream of Buskers entertained the queue. Even the police, theoretically there to shift them, were only half hearted as they moved them a few paces this way or that to comply with the law. When we arrived the duty policeman was actually trying to free an escapologist who couldn't quite make it. Merseyside was always a dangerous place for escapologists, there were too many experts at knots around.

Nearby, a glassy-eyed ballad singer weaved his way gently around the struggling pair giving the 'Rose of Tralee' absolute hell. Dinny nudged me as the singer came abreast.

"'e's 'alf cut," He announced knowledgeably. I looked at the bleary, half closed eyes, as the man held his hat out for offerings. The song stopped as Dinny slipped a button in. "God bless yeh sur, god bless y'." Ten feet further on, with the song unfinished, he checked his takings. Philosophically throwing Dinny's button away, he scooped the remainder and headed for the pub opposite. A quick fourpenny pint and he was at it again at the head of the queue. Four times between our arrival and getting our tickets he vanished and returned, with dire consequences for the Rose of Tralee. By the time we clawed our way up the darkened stairs to the 'Gods' we were in high good humour. I was having the time of my life. The acts, assisted by a raucous and knowledgeable audience, were as good as rumour had had it and as the lights went up for the interval Dinny had a great idea.

"Let's make a night of it," he suggested. I looked at him puzzled.

"Whaddy y' mean?"

"Let's gerra drink down at the bar." Alarm bells rang inside me instinctively. Despite the drunkenness that had always surrounded me, I had never actually touched the stuff.

"Ah come on Li," urged Tom as I hesitated, "I'm goin' away termorrer. "Who knows when we'll gerranother night out."

"OK," I said reluctantly, "But I'm 'avin' Sasparella . . . gorrit?"

"Fair enough," agreed Dinny, rising from his seat and squeezing his way along the darkened alleyway. Minutes later we were pushing and barging our way through the throng round the tiny theatre bar. Tom and I leaned against the wall as Dinny banged on the counter yelling his order above the noise.

"Hey Li, grab these will y'?" I heard him roar. Tom and I took the two pints he was holding high above his head, then he joined us breathlessly as we crashed our way out to the corridor.

"Here y'are Li," he said, triumphantly holding a pint out.

"That's beer," I said after taking a sip, "I said I wanted Sasparella."

"Got none," he said with a grin, "Feller thought I was pullin' 'is leg, honest. Anyroad, get it down y' it'll put 'airs on y' chest." I hesitated. "Go on," he urged, "It won't bite y'. Take a swig."

Trapped between instinctive dislike for the stuff and loyalty to Tom in whose honour we were celebrating, I tried it, it wasn't bad. I took another, bigger swig. Inhibitions fell from me like a discarded coat as I downed the lot in lightheaded ecstasy. I dimly remember Dinny shouting, "There's just time for another."

168

I never did see Wilson, Kepple and Betty perform their Sand Dance although I dimly remember the roars of laughter around me. Nor do I remember leaving the theatre, supported by Dinny and Tom, long before the show was finished as they realised I was plastered and had to be sobered up before I got home. The first thing that came clearly was Aunt Min's agitated voice.

"Jesus," I heard dimly, " 'ell murder 'im'."

"It's my fault," I heard Dinny say as I gasped for breath. "Honest, I shoulda known what'd 'appen."

"Its too bloody late now isn't it?" snapped Aunt Min as my head went under the tap again. The room swam as the rough treatment took effect. Hazy agitated figures wafted about the tiny kitchen as a thousand hammers beat in my head and my stomach heaved.

"Thank God y' 'ad the sense t' bring 'im 'ere first," I heard her say, "Pat'll go mad when 'e sees 'im."

I couldn't have cared less. I just wanted to die, anything to get rid of the overpowering nausea that gripped me. Then I felt a stinging slap across the cheek.

"Li," she hissed, "Wake up y' silly sod. Wake up, it's half past ten."

By a quarter to eleven, soaked, battered and still well under, they dragged me to my feet for the short journey home. Deep down, sudden panic gripped me as enough sense returned to make me aware of my predicament.

"Come with me Aunt Min, please" I gasped.

"We'll all come," said Dinny, "It was my fault, I'll take the blame."

God knows what would have happened if they hadn't come. By the time we reached home the clock had passed the witching hour and Dad was already on the prowl, up and down the front pathway. Long afterwards I learned that his first reaction was near homicidal as they brought me up the path. Only Aunt Min's pleadings saved me from the father of all leatherings with the belt. Between them, she and Mam calmed him down enough to get me inside and sitting down. Head still whirling I heard the words that have stayed with me all my life.

"Any bloody man," he roared savagely, "who puts somethin' in 'is mouth t' take away 'is wits is a fool, an' don't you bloody well forgerrit lad."

I didn't forget it and never have because it was quoted by an expert. God knows, in the grinding poverty they had gone through, he had done it often enough in an effort to escape. I couldn't have had a better teacher. It was a sadder and wiser lad that walked thoughtfully to the Ferry the next day to see Tom off.

"Warra night," said Tom as he plonked his kitbag down as the moment came to say goodbye. "Next time Li, you'll 'ave t' drink it a bit slower mate. It goes t' y' knees too quick."

Head still thumping I grinned feebly, "Don't worry Tom, there won't be a next time. As far as I'm concerned y' cin stuff it."

The warning toot of the ferryboat at the landing stage stopped further discussion.

"That's it then," said Tommy, nodding towards the boat, "Time t' push off." He held his hand out.

"See y'," he said flatly.

"Yeah, see y'," replied Dinny, then with a playful dig in the ribs added with a wink, "Y' wanna watch them Indian Judies mate. They tell me they're 'ot stuff."

Tom's strong handsome face broke into a grin.

"Don't worry Din, I know my way around." He turned to me.

"Cheers Li. Take it easy, an' don't forget t' drop us a line will y'?"

I nodded painfully.

"I will Tom, don't worry, an' I'll let y' know 'ow me new job goes. Thanks again for facin' Dad with me, he'd a bloody well killed me if you all 'adn't bin there."

"Ah 'e's alright," said Tom, " 'e was only worried for y' Li, 'e knows warrit's all about mate, 'e's a good bloke. Y' won't go far wrong if y' listen to 'im an' that's a fact."

He lifted the heavy kitbag on to his right shoulder with

consumate ease, then, with a final wave, headed down the floating bridge to the waiting boat.

13

A Gentleman no less

1937, with its rapid succession of changes which so altered my life, was I suppose, a watershed for me. Pitchforked into new surroundings, meeting Antoinette, my first separation from home and, strangest of all, the sight of poor Bonko inextricably trapped and at seventeen, already condemned to the same treadmill as his father, all crystalised in me a deep, inexplicable yearning to 'improve' myself . . . But how? Anyway, what the devil was it I wanted? Even if I had had someone to talk to I couldn't have explained myself. Several times I had tried, half-heartedly to button-hole Mam or Dad but each time baulked at the last moment. They wouldn't understand. How could they? When for as long as I could remember, their whole lives had been one continuous battle to survive. I felt I knew Dad's answer before I even asked the question. "What the 'ell d'y' want?" he would say, "You've gorra good job, clothes on y' back, an' a full belly, what more d'y' want?"

And he would be right. It was more than he had ever had, more than any of them had had. What I couldn't explain was that I was restless because I was lucky in all these things for it was these things that brought me into contact with a whole host of people who were different. People who dressed well, spoke nicely, people who found entertainment in reading, music, plays and other things which were a part of a world I neither knew nor understood. No, they would think I was crackers. Unfortunately my restlessness bred rebellion, rebellion that very near got me the sack within a month of starting my new job.

It all happened so easily. Unlike the big stations where each man had his particular job and stuck to it, on a rural station everyone pitched in when needed and I needed no second bidding when Mr Andrews, my new boss told me to stand in and porter the 4-15 from Chester when Harry, the duty porter sprained his ankle. Within minutes I was on the platform. The train drew in and discharged just three passengers, two of whom gave me their tickets, but the third, way up at the far end of the platform, waved imperiously to me. I galloped up to the end carriage.

"I say," grumbled the young man, about two years older than myself, and obviously a 'toff' from his dress and manner, "You're jolly slow aren't you?" I bristled inwardly. "I'm sorry sir . . ." I began. He cut me short with an airy wave.

"Never mind that my man," he snapped, "Just get the suitcase, I'm in a hurry."

Fuming, I climbed into the carriage and grabbed the case on the rack and pulled. My arm nearly dropped out of its socket as the case fell and hit the seat like a stone. It seemed to weigh a ton.

"Steady on there," he cried, "What are you trying to do? . . . Ruin the damned thing?"

"I . . ." again he stopped me dead.

"Oh never mind the excuses," he interrupted peevishly, "Just pick it up and follow me."

In a silent fury I did. The platform seemed a mile long. By the time we reached the bottom of the slope leading to the taxi rank outside the station my arms ached. He reached into his pocket.

"That's for your trouble he said grandly, sticking a coin into my hand. I opened my palm and looked at it. A penny! Without thinking I stuck my hand in my own pocket, put another penny to it and handed them to him.

"That's alright sir," I said coldly, "I'm paid for this job. It was no trouble."

White faced with anger he turned on his elegant heel and swept into the station. Within minutes I was in Mr

173

Andrews' office. His ultimatum was short and to the point, 'Apologise or . . .' I knew what the 'or' meant. I apologised and the passenger left with a satisfied smile. I had forgotten, in my new found pride that despite my regular wage and splendid uniform I was still the lowest of the low. How could I explain this behaviour at home, when all their lives they had been forced to take anything that was thrown at them just to keep bread on the table? Who was I, an uneducated moron, to rebel? That seemed to be the answer, education, Antoinette had it. She could cope with almost anything. She even made me feel like a worm without even raising her voice. But how the hell did one get an education without money? I thought momentarily of the advert a few weeks previously in the local paper.

'Be an Accountant by correspondence', it said, 'Two and sixpence down and one and sixpence per week' for the year long course. Without a clue what was involved I thought "Great", that's for me, then I realised I only got two shillings spends a week and I didn't have the heart to worry Mam. Anyway she would probably think I had a slate loose with such ideas. No, I had to find another way.

Two weeks after my near sacking I found another way, well, not so much found a way as got a shock. I was in the bathroom getting ready to take Antoinette to night-school and came downstairs in response to Mam's call that she was in the house waiting for me. I heard Dad's voice through the kitchen door as I stopped to fasten my shirt button before going in.

"I wish t' God Li had an education," he said, bitterness in his voice, " 'e'll get nowhere without it and that's a fact."

I stopped in amazement. He had never mentioned it to me! Mam provided the explanation.

"What chance was there of education Pat? It took us all our time t' live, never mind education, y' need money for that. Anyroad," she continued, " 'es a good lad, 'e'll get by. There's no flies on Li, at least 'es gorra good job an' that's more'n most. Warrabout y'self?" I pricked my ears.

174

It was rare for me to hear any details of their lives before I was born. As far as I was concerned Dad's only interest in all the years I knew him was in trying to get a job, any job to bring a few shillings in. I was never more wrong in my life as I found out when Antoinette's voice came through the door.

"Which school did you go to Mr Sullivan? Oh you don't mind my asking do you?"

Dad laughed. He laughed much more often now that he had regular work.

"No I don't mind luv. I went to a village school in Ireland, not that we learned much mind. We were even poorer there than we were 'ere."

"And you Mrs Sullivan?"

"The same one. That's where we met isn't it Pat?"

"Aye, an' that's about the only good thing that came out of it. Mind you Antoinette, I would have liked a good education."

" 'e reads a lot," broke in Mam, "Always 'as. It's a wonder 'e doesn't get segs on his eyes." I gasped in silent astonishment, I had seen him read of course, many a time, but as far as I knew they were the popular craze, Westerns.

"What kind of books do you read Mr Sullivan? My father has quite a lot, perhaps you could borrow some of them."

"No luv, I don't borrow stuff like that. Books cost money. Y' dad wouldn't want them wanderin' about I know. Anyroad I get them from the library. I suppose I like all sorts really. History, I like that very much. Then a birra Shakespeare y'know, I've read one or two of 'is, not that I understand them all of course, an' then I like travel books."

"Africa, that's what 'e likes," said Mam, "I think 'e must've read every one that's bin out about that place, 'e used t' go there y'know when 'e was at sea."

"But you are well read Mr Sullivan," said Antoinette, surprise in her voice. Dad laughed uproariously.

"It's one thing readin' luv, an' another understandin' what y' read. I try of course, but y' need proper schoolin'

175

for that, that's why I wish Li would read more, 'es young enough t' get an education if 'e went t' nightschool.

"But he does read," cried Antoinette in surprise, "He's always got Dad's books down."

"Well I'll be damned," said Mam, " 'es as deep as a drawn well that one, I've never seen 'im with 'is nose in a book, 'ave you Pat?"

"Can't say I 'ave," replied Dad, obviously puzzled, " 'es never in five minutes, 'es more like a hen on a hot griddle . . . 'ow long 'as he been readin' then?"

"Ever since he came back from that course in Yorkshire. He's forever asking my father questions."

"Well I'll be damned," said Mam again, "Would you believe it? 'e never mentions books 'ere."

"Warrabout nightschool. Does 'e ever mention that when 'e takes y'?"

"Not really," replied Antoinette, "An odd word here and there that's all. I have a feeling he would like to learn, but you know Liam better than I do. He keeps a lot to himself unless he gets mad."

"Talkin' about Li," broke in Mam, "Where the divil is 'e?" I heard her chair creak as she stood up, and raced quietly halfway up the stairs then clumped down to give the impression I had only just arrived.

"Come on Li," she said impatiently as she opened the door, "You'll 'ave Antoinette late if y' not careful." I looked across at Dad as he swivelled in his chair to face me. I daren't ask the question quivering on my lips because he would have known I had been listening, but I needn't have worried. The front door had hardly closed behind us when Antoinette was on to the subject of my joining the nightschool.

"Your mother and father would love you to go," she said after repeating all that I already knew.

"What would I learn?" I countered, suddenly nervous at the thought.

"You study, then you learn," she corrected me.

"Well alright, then, what would I study?"

176

"What would you like to study? Why don't you discuss it with your mother and father? They will help you, they want to help you."

"Never thought about it," I lied. We walked along in silence for a moment or two then she looked at me keenly.

"Now don't take offence," she said suddenly.

"What at?" I asked, "Y 'aven't said nowt yet." She hesitated, then, with unusual bluntness came straight to the point.

"Well first of all you will have to learn to speak properly." I stopped and glared at her in sudden temper.

"What's the marrer with the way I talk?" I demanded, "That's the way I've always talked. What's up with it?"

Her dark eyes flashed resolutely as she faced me in the quiet street.

"There," she said, "I knew it, you're in a temper."

"I'm norrin a flamin' temper," I snapped, "I 'aven't said nothin' . . . yet."

"Yes you are," she persisted, "You're always in a temper about something. One word and, whoops, you go off like a blessed rocket. How can you learn when you do that? Well Liam Sullivan," she continued before I could speak, "You don't scare me. If you want to look silly then that's your business, but I know how you speak and you don't so listen for once."

I watched fascinated as her red lips writhed and wriggled as she mimicked my last statement. It sounded terrible.

"Ah go on," I said disbelievingly, "I don't talk like that."

"Worse," she said, "Mother nearly had a fit when you first came into our house, and I got into terrible trouble for wanting to see you."

"Toffy nosed so . . ."

"Don't you dare call Mummy toffy nosed," she snapped, "She is not toffy nosed, and neither is Daddy. They are nice people and they are my parents and don't you jolly well forget it."

"A . a . ah," I grumbled.

"Look Liam," she snapped impatiently, "That is how

you speak whether you like it or not and people judge you by how you speak and behave. I know what you are like, but strangers don't and there is nothing you can do about it, so don't get mad at me." We walked in stolid silence as I absorbed this blunt fact. Suddenly I made up my mind.

"Right," I said, "I'll show 'em. I'll learn t' speak proper."

"You'll have to do more than just that," she said bluntly, "If you want to learn then you must listen, and before you can listen you will have to learn to control your temper and want to learn . . . oh yes," she added with a hint of a smile, "You will have to learn a few manners too." I gazed at her in blank astonishment.

"Whaddy y' mean, manners?" I demanded. "I use a knife an' fork same as you, don't I? Warram I supposed t' do? A flippin' Fan dance or summat?"

"There you go again," she said accusingly, "Getting all worked up about nothing. It's quite simple really. All you have to do is be reasonable."

"I am flamin' reasonable," I snapped irritably. She stopped abruptly and faced me.

"No you're not damned well reasonable," she cried exasperatedly. "You don't listen, you're pig headed, you're jealous, and you are most unreasonable. Why the devil I go out with you I will never know, so there."

I looked at her in astonishment. No one had ever spoken to me like that before and got away with it except Mam and Dad, I was stuck for an answer.

"You swore," I said accusingly, "An' you a convent girl." She burst out laughing.

"You are enough to make anyone swear, but if you want to get on then you will have to listen and learn so for once be quiet and listen to me."

So absorbed were we that we didn't even notice the nightschool as we walked by, but it was the most illuminating walk I ever took. Only she could have got away with it. She lambasted me, pleaded with me, and finally won me over to the idea of nightschool and study with her. I was made to promise to have a long talk with Mam and Dad about it and to talk her father into lending me some of his books to use at home. I kept the promise and never regretted it. Mam and Dad were a revelation.

Dad had been in a grade called X7 for nearly five years, that being the highest grade, he had no where else to go. Nor was he the only one by a long, long way. He told me that there were many men around the slum area good at school but who, bare footed and often hungry were turned out at eleven, sometimes ten years old and as quickly dragged under and lost in the faceless mass around them. I can see his face now as clearly as I did the day I cornered him in the greenhouse and tackled him about my new ambitions.

"I'm glad t' 'ear it," he said, putting his soil stained hand on my shoulder. "Y' won't regret it, but," he warned bluntly, "Don't bugger about with it. If y' gonna do it, then do it. Me an' y' Mam'll back y' as long as we 'ave a copper t' spare but don't kid y'self, it's not gonna be easy. You'll 'ave t' get y' 'ead down an' keep it down, gorrit? Nothin' comes easy in this world lad, warrever y' get y' gorra pay for it, some 'ow, sometime. You'll gerrout what y' purrin' an' nowt else."

Wondering what the hell I had committed myself to I nodded solemnly. On my return from Antoinette's that night I knew what I had let myself in for as I walked into a family conference.

Declan Donelly, Teresa's boy friend, himself far above our station with a degree from Dublin University, and now in digs down the road, fulfilling his avowed intention of marrying her, greeted me the moment I walked in.

"Ah sure it's himself no less," he said with a grin as he beckoned me to the chair beside him, "Sit y'self and tell me all about it." I gazed at him uncomprehendingly. "The Learnin' Li, I hear tell you've set y' heart on being a gentleman and a scholar?" I flushed scarlet. Teresa laughed.

"He might be a scholar if he works at it Declan, but a gentleman . . ." she blew through her pursed lips. "The way he wolfs his food he'd be more at home in a zoo."

"We 'aven't all bin in posh 'ouses," snapped Mam irately.

"I was only pullin' his leg Mam," said Teresa contritely, "But you've got to 'ave a few manners as well as education t' get on in this world. You know that Mam."

"Well that's easy fixed," announced Declan, "The easiest way to learn table manners is to dine out." I looked at him aghast. Eat out? Except for the odd butty at Dinny's or at some relative I had never eaten out in my life. Dad grinned and gave him a slow wink.

"That's a damned good idea Declan, why don't y' teach 'im?" I could have kicked him.

"Right," broke in Teresa, "You're on." I rose to my feet protesting vigorously. It was one thing going to night-school but this was going crackers. I dug my heels in. Dad's tone changed suddenly as he fixed me with a look.

"Y' say y' want t' get on? Y' wanna mix?" I nodded. "Then do as you're bloody well told. If Declan and Teresa are good enough t' wanna teach y' manners, then you'll flamin' well learn 'em, so shut up." That was it. What started as a half joke suddenly assumed serious proportions. I looked across at Mam in a last appeal and dropped another clanger. She was as enthusiastic as the rest. Our new surroundings had changed her too.

On the following Saturday my training in precise table manners began in earnest at a small restaurant in the main street. Scrubbed, polished and distinctly uneasy, I sat between Declan and Teresa, facing a mound of cream cakes and a china cup and saucer. Compared with my usual pint mug at home it looked like a thimble. Teresa gave me a nod. I took a cake and immediately received a kick on the ankle as I went to take a bite. She took a tiny knife cum fork from beside her plate and held it lightly between finger and thumb as she leaned towards me.

"Y' don't stuff it down you," she hissed, forgetting her aitches, y' cut it, watch."

My mouth watered as she demonstrated. I nodded understandingly and reached with my cream covered hand for my fork. Another surreptitious kick stopped me. I looked at her irritably.

"Wipe y' 'ands on y' napkin y' fool," she hissed again, "Luk at it, it's covered in cream." I glowered and looked across at Declan grinning like a Cheshire cat as he delicately hoisted a tiny piece of cake on the fork in his ham-like fist. He winked.

"Ah sure y' doin' great," he said encouragingly as the piece of cake fell off the fork for the second time. Sudden temper overwhelmed me.

"Ah t' 'ell with the flippin' cake," I snapped, "I'm goin' 'ome."

I felt a stab of pain on my ill-used ankle.

"You'll stay there and eat it," hissed my sister, "And you'll eat it properly if it kills y'." She looked and sounded just like Mam. I hated every sticky crumb of it, but I ate it. Years later I sat in a restaurant in Liverpool, watching a kid stuffing himself. I knew just how he felt as his mother scolded him. Like me, he wanted to get at the cakes and to hell with the frills, but for me it wasn't to be, I had to stick it out. Over the next few weeks we progressed from cakes to salads and other knotty problems as we worked our way through ascending classes of restaurants in and around the town. To me, ever hungry, it seemed as though there was always more cutlery than food, but by Christmas the lessons had sunk in and I was confident enough to try it on my own in a small place on the edge of town. Then, the day after Boxing day 1938, I went berserk.

With my one and only suit discreetly covered by a brand new belted overcoat, hands comfortably esconced in my first pair of leather gloves, and with a touch of the Aga Khans in my manner, I blew the whole of my spends and Christmas boxes on a night out with Antoinette in Liverpool. If ever I win the pools I will know just how it feels. It was great. I was so carried away with the dinner I even had the neck to tip the waiter a shilling. I regretted my largesse next day but it felt great at the time. We didn't arrive home until after eleven but Dad didn't say a word. I vowed there and then that I would take both of them out when I could afford it and, we would have a taxi. It was seven long years before I could finally treat them but it was a grand night when it happened. Mam must have enjoyed it because she cried on the way home.

Once started, and despite the constant leg pulling at work, I flung myself into my self imposed task. Antoinette's Dad gave me the run of his bookshelves and I revelled in them. Her mother, elegant as always, constantly corrected me when I lapsed into the vernacular and I never resented it, but there were mixed feelings in my own family. Aunt Min was impressed even when I put all my 'h's' in the wrong places, but Aunt Sarah, a born Jonah, was adamant.

"It's all wrong," she declared after I had vividly detailed my night out in Liverpool. "You'll see," she warned darkly, " 'e'll be too flamin' stuck up t' talk t' y' before 'es finished. I don't 'old with it an' that's a fact."

"Why don't y' just shurrup luv?" suggested Uncle Mat diplomatically, "Honest, y' get worse woman."

"I don't 'old with all this steppin' outa y' class," she persisted, "No good'll come of it, you'll see."

"What's up with y' Sarah?" snapped Dad irritably, " 'es only goin' t' nightschool an' learnin' t' speak proper. What's wrong with that for God's sake?"

"What's good enough for you should be good enough for 'im," she answered primly. Dad gave her a filthy look.

"What's good enough for me Sarah is not good enough for 'im. Why the 'ell should it be? It's 'is life isn't it. D'y' want the same for 'im as we've 'ad all these years? Look at young Antoinette next door," he added before she could answer. "She's goin' t' college in September. I wish t' God 'e could. There's more t' life than eatin' an' sleepin' y'know."

"I don't 'old with all this education," she sniffed, "It's alright for them lot," she flicked her head in the direction of Antoinette's house, "They're a toffy nosed lot t' start with. It's natural for them isn't it? But it's not for the likes of us. We're workin' class an' we should stay that way I say."

Aunt Min came through the backdoor as Uncle Mat shook his head in disbelief. She sensed the atmosphere at once.

" 'ello," she said with a grin, "Don't tell me! Sarah's put 'er foot in it again."

Mam laughed but said nothing as Aunt Min dropped heavily into the chair kept permanently vacant for her frequent visits. "I suppose it's Li's fault again is it? Steppin' outa 'is class again or some such?" Aunt Sarah sniffed heavily.

"What's it gorra do with you anyroad?" asked Aunt Min, "If 'e got inter trouble an' got the birch you'd be scandalised. If 'e goes t' church too often y' say 'es gerrin t' be an 'oly Joe, so what the bloody 'ell do y' want woman?"

Aunt Sarah remained silent. The forces against her were too great. Even Uncle Mat, well used to her forebodings after all these years, was getting irritable and she knew it. She went off on to another track.

"Anyroad," she said triumphantly, "There's gonna be another war, an' education or no education they'll all 'ave t' go, includin' 'im." She jerked her finger at me.

"Trust you t' luk on the bright side," said Aunt Min scathingly, "But y' wrong. There's not gonna be no war. That feller Chamberlain's just come to an agreement with the other feller."

"I wouldn't trust 'im as far as I could throw 'im," answered Aunt Sarah darkly.

" 'oo?" asked Mam.

" 'itler. Y' can't trust them foreigners."

"Ah shurrup," snapped Aunt Min in exasperation, "Y' make me tired. Anyroad, wharrabout the weddin'?"

I pricked my ears up at the change of conversation. Teresa's approaching wedding in June to the patient Declan was something I was looking forward to immensely. He was a great lad and a great mimic. The fact that he could take Aunt Sarah off to a tee and she had caught him at it did not endear him to her, but even she had to admit he was a good Catholic man, even though he was educated.

"Oh everythin's goin' fine," said Mam enthusiastically. Dad rose rapidly to his feet as she spoke.

"Come on Mat, lets go an' 'ave a jar. This is no place for us." Uncle Mat grinned as he got up.

"You're on Pat. Let's git, before they rope us in." I settled myself down by the fire to listen to the latest news as they left. It wasn't long in coming.

"They're lookin' for an 'ouse now," announced Mam.

"Well they shouldn't 'ave much trouble there," opined Aunt Min, both hands snugged round her cup of tea, "There's plenty of 'ouses about."

"Oh they're not rentin'," said Mam with a note of triumph, "They're buyin'."

"Buyin'?" gasped my two aunts together. Like me they were startled at this news. It just had to be the greatest thing that had happened in our immediate family. True, we were in a better house than we had ever been in but to own one! Well, it was unheard of at our level.

"There!" cried Aunt Sarah triumphantly. All her worst fears realised. "I told y' didn't I? First 'im," she nodded at me, "Now Teresa."

"What the 'ell are y' talkin' about woman?" snapped Aunt Min.

"Big ideas that's warr'ime talkin' about. Buyin' indeed. Never 'eard such nonsense in me life." I looked from one to the other, it was something I had never dreamt could happen either. We had come a long way. The old life had all but gone. Even Dinny I had not seen for months, yet strangely, no longer missed him. I was too busy, too full of the many things I was learning. The trouble was that the more I learned the more I realised how ignorant I was. God, it was bad enough being ignorant without knowing it, but to know you are uncouth and resent it is twice the burden. Still, judging from some I now met it was a comfort to know that intelligence didn't always go with education, nor polished manners with delicacy of feeling

184

for others. Caught between the two worlds as I was, I found it all very confusing.

14

A Bird in the Hand

There was no question about it, Teresa's new house on the edge of town was little short of a palace. I had seen the notice board several times as I drove by on my rounds for the new estate, but I never dreamt that my own sister would own one. Nor was I alone in this, Aunt Sarah even now, three months after the wedding, had not fully recovered from the shock she got when she heard the price, six hundred pounds.

"That's a hundred pounds for each room in it," she gasped when Mam told her that the deal was done.

"Burr'it's brand new with two lavatories and a garden," snapped Aunt Min as they all sat in our kitchen after the first inspection. "And the bathroom," she enthused, "Did y' see it? It's even got wanna them new fangled whatchamacallits."

"A shower," interpreted Mam helpfully.

"Yeah, that's it, squirts all over y'," said Aunt Min rubbing it in gleefully. "Imagine it," she laughed, "A bit different t' the old 'All Overs' in the kitchen eh. Mary?"

"Aye," replied Mam proudly, "They've done well thank God, an' good luck to 'em."

"Aye, but 'ow are they gonna furnish it?" asked Aunt Sarah forebodingly, "Orange boxes I shouldn't wonder. At that price they can't afford nothin' else I'll bet."

"Don't worry," snapped Mam, "Declan's not daft, 'e knows warr'es doin'. Anyroad, 'es gorra good job 'asn't 'e?"

She was right. My new brother-in-law, with his degree to back him up, did have a good job in the shipping offices in Liverpool, and his success added fuel to the fires of my own ambitions.

With him and Teresa now on the borders of being 'toffs' themselves I could hardly wait for Antoinette to come home from a visit to relatives after the completion of her first year to tell her all the news. It seemed incredible that in just one more short year she would actually be a teacher. Then I would have to watch my 'p's' and 'q's' and no mistake. Already her letters were more like tutorials in her efforts to keep me to my promise. She needn't have worried, I was having a great time. But even in the best of worlds there is usually a fly in the ointment somewhere and mine was an overweight, freckled faced, seventeen year old nymphomaniac, Esther, the boss's daughter. She ogled, cooed, fluttered her pale blue eyes and wiggled her stern on every possible occasion. Several times she had cornered me during the quiet periods of the afternoons. So much so that Ernie, the booking clerk, whose intimate knowledge of women contrasted sharply with his angelic appearance, gave me repeated warnings of what would happen if I was slow on my feet.

"Make no mistake Li, she'll 'ave y' mate if y' not careful. I'd keep me eye on 'er if I was you." 'Keep my eye on her', he must have been kidding. With her shape you couldn't miss her on a foggy night. She was enormous in every sense. Every nerve in my body screamed its warning as she simpered and undulated towards me, but the boss doted on her, I had to be careful. He was a strict disciplinarian who frowned on almost everything except work. He was so straight laced I'll swear he conducted sexual relations with his wife by post, I reckon Esther came by mail order. On the other hand Ernie was quietly lecherous and on several occasions the boss had nearly caught him following his hobby of assessing the female passengers' potential as they wiggled their way up the slope leading from the ticket office to the platform.

"Watch this one Li," he would say during the odd slack period when I had nothing particular to do. I would join him eagerly at his small window to follow his expert commentary as his latest passenger climbed the slope.

"Bit thin around the ankle, but not bad Li. She's gorrit all there lad, just luk at that stern waggle," he would say with satisfaction, noting the port to starboard action of the vanishing rump. He must have had x-ray eyes. To within four or five paces he could tell me authoritatively whether the subject was wearing stays, corsets, long or short drawers, or whether her stockings were held up by a girdle or just old-fashioned garters. In all the time I knew him he never got above the waistline, nor did he attempt a dissertation of the front half. I can only assume he examined that section as they returned at the end of the day. Approval or disapproval of the subject was expressed by a series of Coo's, Cor's, Cor Blimey's or perhaps, when a prime specimen came along, with a quick hiss of indrawn breath as though words had failed him.

It was just a week before Antoinette was due home that near disaster struck. Ernie, with little to do until the five o'clock business train was due, had just settled against his counter to watch a lone passenger head up the slope for the 4.30 p.m. upline. I joined him and together we watched her shimmy her way up. Suddenly Harry, the porter, his platform trolley loaded to the gills from the 4.15 downline, appeared at the top. Absorbed in the passenger, we did not see him bump the wall with his unwieldy load. Seconds later there was a yell as the passenger raised her head, saw the trolley and jammed herself against the wall. Her scream alarmed Harry, hidden behind the mound of crates and parcels. He over-reacted, pulled hard and jammed his hand between the trolley and the wall then let go in agony. I rocketed from the office to give him a hand.

"Hold it Harry," I yelled as I dashed up the slope, "Watch the passenger."

Too late. The trolley brushed her shoulder as it bounced off the wall. She screamed anew as I cannoned into her, bounced off and hit the parcels. Harry's irate voice came over the top as the load cascaded on to the slope.

"The Hen," he yelled, "it's gerrin out."

"What?" I yelled, distractedly trying to help the

woman to her feet as the trolley jammed itself for the second time.

"The 'en!"

"What 'en?"

"That bloody 'en . . . oh sorry missus, I didn't see you there," he apologised. He needn't have bothered. With her hat jammed over her head she couldn't see him either.

"Gerrit quick," he added, pointing frantically at the plump Rhode Island Red struggling to escape its fractured cage. I missed it by a fraction.

"Keep it in the station," yelled Harry desperately as the frightened bird fluttered madly around, "Don't lerrit out or we'll never catch it."

He must have been joking. I had a fleeting glimpse of the passenger, hat now on the side of her head, eyes staring disbelievingly at the mound of parcels around her and two maniacal railway men thrashing frantically about as the chase headed up the slope.

"Don't lerrit on the platform," he shrieked "The 4.15 express is due any minute on the upline." "God," I thought, as I jumped desperately at the bird fluttering above my head. "That goes through like the clappers."

"If it 'its that," shouted Harry and confirming my worst fears, "It won't need pluckin' I'll tell y'."

A split second later I crashed into something soft.

"Wha . . . Wha . . . What . . .?" It was Mr Andrews. I looked up into the cherry red face.

"The 'en's gorrout," I yelled, all my aitches forgotten in my growing excitement.

"I can see that," he yelled back exasperatedly, "Gerrit."

This wasn't a request, this was the voice of authority but I couldn't oblige. With Harry in hot pursuit the bird had already vanished up the slope and on to the platform.

"The upline express," yelled the boss, "The bird'll be killed."

If they met head on that would definitely be an understatement. Up and down the platform, with the 4.30 passengers cheering us on we raced after the fluttering fugitive. Then the bird, the only sane one among us, headed for the waiting room and a bit of peace.

It was sitting quietly on the table as Harry and I burst in. Neither of us noticed Esther, sitting goggle eyed in the corner as she watched us stalk it. It rose with a squawk as Harry pounced and missed, then there was a terrified shriek as it landed on Esther's lap. She leapt on to the seat screaming her head off and holding her skirts way above any possible point of danger. Harry stopped dead in his tracks as he caught sight of the huge expanse of thighs.

"Cor, strike a light," he muttered, with a slow appreciative wink at me. I looked at them. Incongruously they reminded me of a piece of music I had recently heard in Liverpool, yes of course, Tchaikovsky's 'Nut Cracker Suite'.

"Sit down Esther," I called quietly, "You'll frighten the flippin' thing."

Lowering her skirts disappointedly she obeyed, then froze again as the hen returned to her lap.

"Don't move," I hissed, creeping towards her, "Just sit still an' I'll grab it."

Harry stood breathless as I crept to within a foot of her. I grabbed, and as the hen rose with a wild screech I realised, that for the first time in my life, I had a generous handful of a lady's breast.

"Coo," said Esther gratefully. The tableau froze as Mr Andrews stentorian voice rang through the room.

" 'ave y' gorrit?" he yelled irately.

" 'e sure 'as," said Harry gleefully.

With his daughter caught in flagrante delicto, skirts well above her knees, her breast being grasped like a life belt, and an ecstatic look on her face, there was no way I could explain that it was the hen's fault. I didn't even try. With Harry choking from suppressed laughter, I passed the boss in a blur of movement and headed for the safety of the booking office.

The weeks that followed were strained. Esther, under strict parental edict, gazed wistfully at me from afar, but at least I had gone up in Ernie's estimation.

"Fancy," he said, Harry had regaled him with the details, "An 'andful of that. Cor blimey mate, y' deserve a medal."

I didn't get one. As a matter of fact I was a little puzzled why I was still at the station at all. With my nineteenth birthday well past, and a full man's pay of £2:4:4d in my pocket for the past month, I was still doing a junior van driver's job.

"It's all this trouble brewin'," opined Ernie authoritatively when I mentioned it, "Y'know, the war an' everythin'."

"Y' kiddin'. There's not gonna be one. I saw that feller Chamberlain wavin' his bit of paper on the pictures."

"What the 'ell does 'e know?" said Harry scathingly. He didn't like politicians.

"Well 'e should flamin' well know shouldn't 'e?" snapped Ernie, " 'e gets paid for the bloody job doesn't 'e?" It had been the same ever since Chamberlain had come back from Germany, talk, talk, talk. Not that I took much notice of it myself, I had too much to think about, besides Antoinette was due home and I was just itching for the chance to dazzle her with my progress towards being somebody. The trouble was the everybody seemed to be better off somehow. The knots of men that had hung hopelessly round the street corners for years seemed to be thinning out as the shipyard became busier. In fact everything seemed to be changing. Women on our old district through which I passed on my way to work, now wore coats instead of shawls. They looked less haggard than during the bad times, yet for all that there wasn't as much laughter as there used to be.

Even Mam, better off now than in any time in her life, had seemed bitter the night before Antoinette was due home.

"Oh yeah," she snapped to some remark of Aunt Min's, "Things are better alright, but it's taken another bloody war scare t' do it."

"Aye," replied Dad, with a sidelong glance at me, "They're the ones that'll 'ave t' cope with it though. More

191

cannon fodder. An' what'll it solve eh? Sod all, the same as last time. Make y' bloody laugh," he added bitterly.

" 'omes fit for 'ero's t' live in they said," added Mam, "some 'omes hey?"

"Middens more like," agreed Aunt Min, all her jollity gone for once. "They promised the earth an' what did they get? Bugger all except the Means Test an' now the daft sods 'ave started all over again. It'd make y' bloody sick wouldn't it?"

"It'll be a damned sight worse next time," said Jimmy, my brother-in-law, soberly. "This time it won't only be the soldiers doin' the fightin' I'll tell y'."

"Whaddy y' mean?" asked Dad.

"Well we'll all be in it won't we?"

" 'ow come?"

"Aeroplanes," said Jimmy emphatically, "This'll be the front line, not Flanders."

"Aw come off it Jim. They can't reach this far can they? Anyroad, we've got planes too y'know."

"I wouldn't like t' bet on it," answered Jimmy scathingly. "Don't worry. If 'itler starts anythin' 'ell throw the flamin' lot at us, especially the ports, an' we're a port aren't we? Wanna the biggest. 'e'll be after us an' no mistake. Anyone as says different is kiddin' theirselves."

With long practise I sensed a real cracking argument brewing and I wanted no part of it. Quietly I slid up to my room, shut the door, took down the third of the Wodehouse books to which I had become addicted, and escaped into the Mad world of Bertie Wooster. I would far rather be in Blandings Castle with him and potty Lord Emsworth than arguing the toss down there.

The next day, the second of September, with Antoinette due home, the world seemed bright again. I ignored the black headlines of the morning paper and began, with growing excitement, to get ready to meet her. By two o'clock, dressed in my best and smelling like a second class gigolo I stood, complete with gloves and rolled up paper to give the final touch, on the platform at Lime

Street Station. The minutes seemed like hours as I craned my neck to see round the curving platform. At last it came. Momentarily I panicked as the hurrying passengers thinned and there was no sign of her. Then, with a thrill I spotted the pale oval face framed in its long black hair at the very end of the platform. All elegance gone I hurled myself madly along and came to a shuddering halt in front of her. All the words I had so carefully rehearsed for the past few days vanished as my mouth dried up. Instead I gazed at her like a love sick calf. She stood and gazed shyly back at me. I wanted to fling my arms around her, to hug her, to kiss those moist quivering lips. Instead I said, "Hi ya?" I had even forgotten my flaming aitches. A split second later I was in heaven. For the very first time she flung her arms around me and planted a smacker right on my lips. I felt myself go crimson as I imagined every eye on the platform focused on me then, in a reflex action, I squeezed her so tight she cried out.

Throughout the afternoon I walked on air and scarcely heard the newspaper boys screaming their messages of impending doom as I awaited the moment I had planned so long, a dinner dance. We had the lot, in a full rehearsal for the outing I had planned for Mam and Dad on the following Saturday as a surprise. We had a taxi from the house to take us through the tunnel and back. A dinner during which I took every opportunity to display my prowess with the cutlery. We danced the evening away in a state of dream like euphoria and the flashing lights of the tunnel as we came home reminded me of the pleasures to come for Mam and Dad in just one short week.

On Sunday, hand in hand, we went to ten o'clock Mass, then took a quiet dreamy walk through the park. At eleven fifteen we walked into the house. It was so quiet I thought they had all gone out. As I opened the kitchen door Dad whipped his head round savagely as the whole family sat huddled around the wireless sitting on its corner shelf. "Sssh," he hissed as a man's melancholy voice droned from the set. Still standing fixedly in the doorway, we listened to the wavering voice.

"This morning, the British Ambassador in Berlin handed the German Government a final note stating that, unless we heard from them by eleven o'clock that they were prepared at once to withdraw their troops from Poland, a state of war would exist between us. I have to tell you that no such undertaking has been received, and that consequently this country is at war with Germany."

I didn't know it then, but my tiny, unimportant world, had just fallen to pieces. Mam's hand went to her mouth in an involuntary action.

"Mother'v God," she exclaimed, "not again!"

I felt like a sacrificial lamb as all eyes turned towards me. A tiny hand slipped quietly into mine and squeezed it tightly as I looked at Dad and realised with a sense of shock that his eyes were moist with scarce held tears. He rose and came towards me and placed a rough hand silently on my shoulder.

"Please God you'll be alright." he said simply.

A month to the day, I left for a world that was to be at once terrifying yet at times hilarious. I was to see a new life, to behold sights that no man's eyes should be called upon to see . . . but that is another story.

THE END